IMAGI

Ear

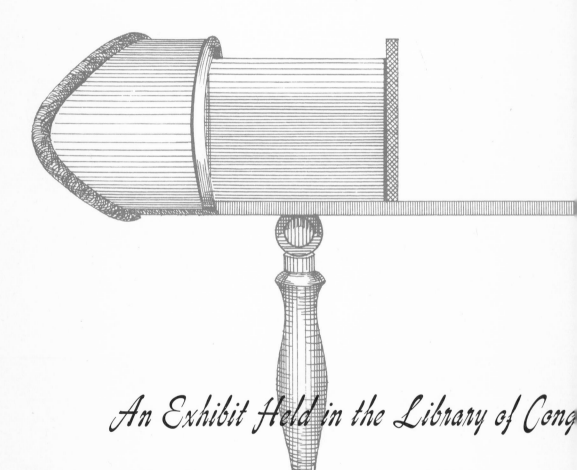

An Exhibit Held in the Library of Cong

OF AMERICA

hotography, 1839-1900

A CATALOG

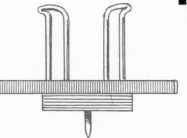

ashington, D. C. - Opened on February 8, 1957

LIBRARY OF CONGRESS • Washington : 1957

L. C. Card, 57–60038

FOR SALE BY THE SUPERINTENDENT OF DOCUMENTS, U. S. GOVERNMENT PRINTING OFFICE
WASHINGTON 25, D. C.   PRICE $1.00

Contents

Foreword

THIS photographic exhibition was arranged in conjunction with the International Exposition of Photography held in Washington on March 22–31, 1957. In this catalog are listed entries describing what was exhibited, together with a few facts about the significance of the items.

From its beginnings over 100 years ago, photography has provided a medium of visual communication that has been probably as important in its impact as the invention of printing from movable type. While the camera obscura had long been known in principle by scholars, the daguerreotype technique of taking pictures, by actually fixing the images on sensitized plates, opened the door to the process of photography. After beholding the early results, Lewis Gaylord Clark wrote in the New York magazine, *The Knickerbocker:*

"We have seen the views taken in Paris by the 'Daguerreotype' and have no hesitation in avowing that they are the most remarkable objects of curiosity and admiration, in the arts, that we ever beheld. Their exquisite perfection almost transcends the bounds of sober belief. Let us endeavor to convey to the reader an impression of their character. Let him suppose himself standing in the middle of Broadway, with a looking glass held perpendicularly in his hand, in which is reflected the street, with all that there is, for two or three miles, taking in the haziest distance. Then let him take the glass into the house, and find the impression of the entire view, in the softest light and shade vividly retained upon its surface."

One of the main disadvantages of the daguerreotype process was that the exposures were long; consequently any movement of people left the effect in the picture of fleeting ghosts. Because of this limitation, street scenes were usually photographed without people. Another shortcoming of the daguerreotype was that each picture was unique and could not be duplicated except by being rephotographed. With such limiting factors, it is remarkable that any pictures have survived from that early period. The prints from daguerreotypes and glass plates in this exhibition were made from the originals, reproducing them as they appear with scratches and defects, including cracks in the plates.

The selection of pictures in the exhibition was made on the basis of the importance of subject in depicting various aspects of American history, life, and progress, rather than on technical excellence. The arrangement is according to subject categories and is roughly chronological. An extensive search was made through thousands of items in the Library's files of photographic materials, including such special collections as the Brady and Brady-Handy photographic files, and the extensive stereograph collections.

The exhibition was assembled in the hope that it would make the photographic resources of the Library better known and encourage the further use of them. A reference work that may be helpful to those interested in information about the collections is the *Guide to the Special Collections of Prints and Photographs in the Library of Congress*, compiled by Paul Vanderbilt, formerly Chief of the Prints and Photographs Division.

The Library of Congress acknowledges its gratitude to the George Eastman House in Rochester for the loan of photographic equipment; to Beaumont Newhall, curator of the George Eastman House, for his essay "American Photography, 1839–1900"; to the U. S. National Museum of the Smithsonian Institution for the loan of daguerreotypes; and to Mark H. Brown of Alta, Iowa, for the loan of photographs by L. A. Huffman. The catalog was prepared by Nelson R. Burr, who also did the research.

HERBERT J. SANBORN
Exhibits Officer, Library of Congress.

VIII

American Photography, 1839-1900

by Beaumont Newhall

PHOTOGRAPHY came to America from France in the fall of 1839. The first news was brought by Samuel F. B. Morse, who visited Daguerre in the spring, while the daguerreotype process was still the secret of its inventor. In a letter to the *New York Observer*, April 20, 1839, he described with a painter's eye the pictures which Daguerre had made; they were, he said, "Rembrandt perfected," and he held out such optimistic promises for the process that on his return to America he at once saw to it that Daguerre was elected an Honorary Member of the National Academy of Design.

The French Government published Daguerre's process at an open meeting of the Academy of Science and the Academy of Fine Arts in Paris on August 19. Shortly thereafter an instruction book was printed. Morse boasted to Daguerre that as soon as he received the first copy of the booklet to arrive in America he at once began to make daguerreotypes. His first success, a picture of the Unitarian Church in New York, was put on view on September 27. He was not the first American photographer, however, for a certain D. W. Seager had already taken a daguerreotype. Within weeks others were practicing the newly discovered art, notably John W. Draper, Joseph Saxton, Robert Cornelius, Alexander S. Wolcott, and John Johnson. These pioneers worked with homemade cameras built from Daguerre's plans, they made their own materials, and somehow by trial and error achieved success.

Although the instruction manual (which was reprinted in America by popular demand) fully explained the process, the skill of hand required for perfection could not be mastered withou personal instruction. François Gouraud, Daguerre's pupil and agent for the sale of apparatus, arrived in New York on November 23, 1839. The following week he put a collection of daguerreotypes on display and gave lessons. The pictures were finer than anything which Morse and his colleagues had produced, and they became his eager students. Gouraud traveled on to Providence, R. I., and Boston, where his demonstrations drew crowds of the curious. While in Boston he published a booklet, summarizing his lectures and containing a description of how to take portraits.

The daguerreotype process, as Daguerre described it, consisted of polishing the surface of a silver-plated copper sheet 6½ x 8½ inches in size until it was mirror bright. It was then put in a box over particles of iodine; the fumes arising formed silver iodide, which was sensitive to light. The plate was exposed in a bulky box camera and afterward developed with heated mercury, which formed an amalgam in proportion to the lights and shades of the original subject. A quick wash in sodium thiosulphate removed the unaffected silver iodide, and a rinse in water completed the operation.

Exposures were at first minutes long. A daguerreotype of King's Chapel, Boston, taken by Gouraud's pupil Samuel Bemis in 1840, required an exposure of 40 minutes. Under these conditions portraiture was impractical. Both Morse and Draper, who claimed to have made portraits in September or October, subjected members of their family to the trial of sitting in the blazing sun with closed eyes for 10 minutes or more with faces whitened with flour. Of these pioneer attempts, nothing remains.[1]

A third team of experimenters—John Johnson and Alexander Wolcott—designed a new type of camera specifically for portraiture. Instead of a lens they used a concave mirror, and the resulting image was more brilliant than the one formed by the front end of a telescope which Daguerre fitted into his camera. Their first results, believed to have been made in October 1839, were miniatures half the size of a postage stamp. They soon improved their camera to make pictures 2 x 2½ inches. Portraits by their associate, Henry Fitz, now in the Smithsonian Institution, are in all probability the earliest existing portrait daguerreotypes made anywhere in the world.

In 1840 two technical improvements had been made in the daguerreotype process which reduced exposures to seconds and made portraiture entirely feasible. Josef Petzval of Vienna designed a lens which admitted more than 16 times the light of Daguerre's meniscus, and John Frederick Goddard of London increased the sensitivity of the daguerreotype plate by fuming it with chlorine as well as iodine. Apparatus more compact than Daguerre's was built for smaller-sized plates.

Portrait galleries now opened in every major city, and traveling daguerreotypists in carts fitted up as studios visited the smaller towns. Thousands upon thousands of portraits taken by these humble and often unknown operators exist. Usually of the "one-sixth" size (2¾ x 3¼ in.), and fitted into imitation leather or plastic cases, they often have a certain naive charm, but seldom any value beyond sharp, clear-cut likenesses of forgotten ancestors.

A few daguerreotypists stand out as artists. In Boston the firm of Albert Sands Southworth and Josiah Johnson Hawes—both of whom were pupils of Gouraud—produced some of the finest portrait daguerreotypes ever made. They boasted that "one of the partners is a practical daguerreotypist" and were proud of the fact that, unlike most gallery proprietors, they did not employ operators, as cameramen were called. The portraits they made of famous men in the 1850's are outstanding in their characterization and simplicity of their composition. The firm undertook difficult, unconventional assignments: a schoolroom with teacher and pupils by "available light"; a

reenactment of a surgical operation taken in the Massachusetts General Hospital; square-riggers in drydock.

The most famous name in early American photography is that of Mathew B. Brady. In 1843, while engaged in making cases for jewelry and for surgical instruments, he offered to supply cases for daguerreotypes. A year later he opened his own daguerreotype gallery on Broadway, and set about forming a "Gallery of Illustrious Americans," a part of which was published in lithographic reproduction in 1850. A quantity of portraits from Brady's collection is now in the Library of Congress. It is not clear how many of these striking and priceless portraits of great historic Americans were actually taken by Brady. It appears that he acted as a collector and historian rather more than as a practical photographer, and that he commissioned portraits or purchased them from other photographers. Individual credits were not the fashion of the day.

In England, simultaneously with the announcement of the daguerreotype process, William Henry Fox Talbot published a radically different technique of photography that made use of paper negatives, from which prints could be made in any quantity. The process, known in its improved state as "calotype," was patented in the United States. Little use was made of it, however, apart from an impressive set of views of New York City taken by Victor Prevost, a Frenchman who came to America as a colorist.

By the late 1850's, both the daguerreotype and the calotype processes were completely displaced by the wet collodion technique, invented in 1851 by the Englishman Frederick Scott Archer. The photographer coated sheets of glass with light-sensitive collodion immediately before using them. Because the plates retained their sensitivity only while wet, photographers had to have darkrooms available wherever they went. Some fitted up wagons as field laboratories, others went to the labor of setting up light-tight tents. Bother-

---

[1] Draper sent Sir John F. W. Herschel a daguerreotype portrait of his sister on July 28, 1840, which for years was considered the first photographic portrait. Circumstantial evidence, when carefully weighed, points to a date for the production of this portrait not long before its shipment to Herschel. Unfortunately this incunabulum of photography was destroyed in an attempt to clean it in 1933.

some as the process was, it yielded negatives of great delicacy and detail, which were printed on paper coated with albumen and silver salts and toned brown in the processing.

The glass negative, which had a whitish deposit to represent the highlights, appeared positive when backed by black. This direct positive was named "ambrotype" in America. A similar technique, which made use of sheets of iron japanned black or chocolate color instead of glass, was known as "ferrotype," or "tintype." The ambrotype, which imitated in its appearance and presentation the daguerreotype, had but a short life, and died in the sixties. The tintype lingered on well into the present century. It became the most popular form of picturemaking until the snapshot replaced it for informal portraits and records of good times.

Two other special applications of the collodion process met with favor in America: cartes-de-visite and stereographs. The former were portraits on mounts 2½ x 4 inches, approximately the size of a visiting card. They were taken eight at a time on a single negative with a multilens camera popularized by Adolphe-Eugène Disdéri in 1854. The cost per picture was radically reduced, and portraits were produced by the thousand. The carte-de-visite system was also used to multiply pictures of famous people. Slip-in albums were sold to keep them in, and soon no Victorian parlor was complete without a bulky plush-covered book with fancy clasps alongside the stereoscope and a basket of stereoscopic pictures.

The skeleton-type viewer, which replaced the awkward box-type stereo viewer, was the invention of Oliver Wendell Holmes around 1863. "Stereographs," as Holmes called the twin-pictures which appeared in three dimensions when seen in his viewer, were taken all over the world and sold like books by dealers. Americans excelled in stereoscopic work, and pioneered in improving the technique to such a point that instantaneous photographs were taken of Broadway in New York, choked with traffic and pedestrians.

The War Between the States gave Mathew B. Brady his greatest opportunity to record history with the camera. He went to the front, organized teams of combat photographers, and produced the remarkable collection of several thousand "Photographic Views of the War" which were published by Anthony. The negatives of this priceless documentation are now preserved in the Library of Congress and the National Archives. The list of those who contributed to this collection is still incomplete, but the outstanding photographers were Alexander Gardner (who left Brady to establish his own collection during the war), Timothy H. O'Sullivan, and George M. Barnard. By a curious coincidence George S. Cook, of Charleston, S. C., who had been employed in New York by Brady, became the chief combat photographer for the Confederacy. Taken as a whole, the photographic documentation of the Civil War is a landmark. No such complete pictorial record of warfare had ever been put together before. The impact of these stark images which, as Brady stated, "present grim-visaged war exactly as it appears" has seldom been excelled even today. Unable to photograph action, Brady and his men concentrated upon the ravages of war—ruined buildings, hasty emplacements—and the men who did the fighting, posed informally outside their quarters or within fortifications. Some of the photographs of corpses lying where they fell are among the strongest indictments of war ever recorded. "It was so nearly like visiting the battlefield to look over those views," wrote Oliver Wendell Holmes on returning from the front, "that all the emotions excited by the actual sight of the strained and sordid scene, strewed with rags and wrecks, came back to us, and we buried them in the recesses of our cabinet as we would have buried the mutilated remains of the dead they too vividly represented."

When hostilities ceased, America began to explore the vast and virtually unknown areas beyond the Mississippi. Photographers accompanied the official Government expeditions. T. H. O'Sullivan was photographer to Clarence King's Geological Exploration of the Fortieth Parallel in 1867; in 1870 he was in Panama; and from 1871 to 1873 he explored Arizona and New Mexico Territories with Lt. George M. Wheeler. His photographs of the Canyon de Chelle are memorable; his records of vanishing Indian tribes are historically and ethnologically invaluable. Alexander Gardner drove his photographic buggy across Kansas, photographing the building of the transcontinental railroad, the

Union Pacific. John Wesley Powell reported his exploration of the Grand Canyon with photographs taken, for the most part, by John K. Hillers. Photographs of the Yellowstone area, taken by William Henry Jackson in 1872, were used to persuade Congress to create the Yellowstone National Park. Jackson became the chief expeditionary photographer in the country, returning summer after summer to the Rocky Mountains and the West. He packed a 20- x 24-inch view camera to mountain peaks—along with the inseparable dark tent for, like every photographer in the land, he was using the wet collodion process. Many so-called "dry plate" techniques were proposed to simplify photography, but all proved impractical until an English physician, Richard Leach Maddox, proposed the use of gelatin for binding the light-sensitive silver salts to glass. The year of this great discovery was 1871; by 1880 the gelatin process rendered the collodion technique obsolete.

The new material could be prepared in advance, and could be processed at the photographer's convenience. No longer was he chained to a darkroom. He was also able to dispense with a tripod, for gelatin plates were so much more sensitive that snapshots regularly became possible. New cameras were designed, boxlike and inconspicuous. Amateurs everywhere began to photograph people unawares with their "detective cameras." To capture swift action became their goal. As one photographer wrote in 1885: "The amateur feels a peculiar desire to 'take something,' and if the 'something' be an animate object unconscious of his presence so much the better, and with what a thrill does he see his first 'snapshot' develop up, whether a railroad train, a trotting horse, or a man hurrying along the ground . . ."

In this very year Eadweard Muybridge repeated in Philadelphia with dry plates what he had accomplished in 1878 under a brilliant California sky with wet plates. He had photographed a horse in full gallop, in 12 successive exposures of $\frac{1}{500}$ second each. The pictures were a revelation to the world; nobody had observed the legs of a swiftly moving animal. Muybridge was invited by the University of Pennsylvania to continue his work there, and produced under the title *Animal Locomotion* a series of over 750 action photographs of all kinds of animals in motion and human figures engaged in a wide variety of action.

With the invention of the Kodak camera by George Eastman, photography entered a new era. Eastman, who began as an amateur in the wet collodion days, opened in 1880 one of the first gelatin dry plate factories in America. He then put on the market a roll holder for paper film, which William Henry Jackson found "a new power placed in our hands . . . whereby our labors are made sport." Eastman's next invention was the Kodak (a name he coined). It was a simple box camera, loaded with enough roll film to make a hundred pictures, each $2\frac{1}{2}$ inches in diameter. Anybody who could press a button could make pictures with it. When exposure No. 100 had been made, the entire camera was returned to the factory in Rochester, N. Y., where the film was developed and printed and returned. The Kodak was a phenomenal success. Thirteen thousand were sold between its introduction in July 1888 and September 1889.

Eastman clearly recognized that there were two classes of amateur photographers, the picture-makers, "who devote time enough to acquire skill in developing, printing, toning, &c.," and those "who, lacking some, or all, of the requisites of the 'true amateur' desire personal pictures or memoranda of their every-day life, objects, places or people that interest them in travel, &c." He designed the Kodak for the latter.

Serious amateurs began to form societies and to exhibit their work, seeking recognition for photography as an art form. The leader of this new movement was Alfred Stieglitz, and by the time the century ended, American pictorial photography had won international recognition.

Catalog of Entries

IMAGE OF AMERICA

Early Photography, 1839-1900

An Exhibition

Part One: 1839-1869

Birth of Photography in the United States

1. NICÉPHORE NIEPCE, FIRST PHOTOGRAPHER: 1765–1833

Photograph of frontispiece to Alphonse Davanne, *Nicéphore Niepce, Inventeur de la Photographie* (1885).

The sculptor of this statue (at Chalon-sur-Saône, the inventor's birthplace in France) symbolized his contribution by the photographic plate in his hand. After years of experimenting, in 1822 Niepce produced a heliographic reproduction on glass in the camera, using a kind of asphalt that hardens upon exposure to light. About 4 years later he made heliographic etchings on metal, instead of glass. In 1827 he made his first camera photograph of the courtyard of his farm. LC–USZ62–10992

2. LOUIS J. M. DAGUERRE, PERFECTER OF PHOTOGRAPHY: 1789–1851

Photographic copy by Mathew B. Brady from a daguerreotype taken in 1848 at Daguerre's home in France, by Charles R. Meade of New York.

Ironically, Daguerre did not like to be photographed! His interest in light images was inspired by his early work as a skilled contriver of scenic and lighting effects for operas. In 1829 he agreed to work with Niepce to improve his heliographic asphalt process, and later he discovered the sensitivity to light of iodide of silver, and the use of mercury vapor to develop latent images on plates. LC–BH8331–568

3. SAMUEL F. B. MORSE, FATHER OF AMERICAN PHOTOGRAPHY: 1791–1872

From a wet plate taken by Brady or an assistant when Morse was 75 years old.

Like Daguerre, Morse became interested in photography through painting. While in Paris, trying to interest the French Government in his telegraphic system in the winter of 1838–39, he met with Daguerre, who invited him to his studio to view his daguerreotypes. Morse was so enthusiastic that after his return to America he had apparatus made and started to experiment.

LC–BH82–1963

4. PROFESSOR MORSE IS INTRODUCED TO PHOTOGRAPHY: 1839

Note from Samuel F. B. Morse to Louis J. M. Daguerre, March 1, 1839. Photostat from pencil draft, Morse Papers, Manuscript Div.

Learning that Morse was in Paris, Daguerre invited him to his studio. Morse replied by this note, drafted in English for translation into French, requesting a postponement of the appointment to view the "most interesting experiment." A few days later, after seeing it, Morse excitedly reported what he had viewed in a letter to his brothers.

5. MORSE INVITES DAGUERRE TO EXHIBIT IN AMERICA: 1839

Letter, Samuel F. B. Morse to Louis J. M. Daguerre, May 20, 1839. Photostat from pencil draft, Morse Papers, Manuscript Div.

Morse returned to America in April, so impressed by Daguerre's discovery that he proposed his election as an honorary member of the National Academy of Design, of which he was president. In this letter Morse assured Daguerre of his readiness to defend his title to the discovery, and suggested a display of his photographs in the United States. Daguerre was grateful, but regretted that his negotiations to have the French Government acquire his invention would forbid an exhibit.

6. AMERICANS GET EXCITED ABOUT PHOTOGRAPHY: 1839

Letter from Samuel F. B. Morse to François Dominique Arago, May 20, 1839. Photostat from pencil draft, Morse Papers, Manuscript Div.

The letter reflects the excitement which the news of daguerreotypy aroused in the United States. With his usual generosity, Morse suggested American aid to Daguerre, and offered his own services. Probably he had talked about the discovery with his colleagues on the faculty of the University of the City of New York (now New York University), where he was professor of painting and sculpture.

6a. FRANCOIS GOURAUD, EARLY DAGUERREOTYPE INSTRUCTOR: 1840

Letter, François Gouraud to Nathan Hale, Jr., editor, *Boston Daily Advertiser*, New York, February 14, 1840. Photostat from Hale Family Papers, Manuscript Div.

Gouraud came to the United States in November 1839 as Louis J. M. Daguerre's agent, bringing a collection of the best daguerreotypes taken by Daguerre and his pupils. He traveled about the country, lecturing on the daguerreotype, and one of his pupils was Samuel F. B. Morse. Early in 1840 he went to Boston, where he sold apparatus, gave instructions, and published a condensation of Daguerre's manual—one of the first photographic books issued in America. He paved the way for his Boston visit by this letter to Hale, who was a nephew of the Revolutionary hero, Nathan Hale, and brother of Edward Everett Hale, author of *The Man Without a Country*.

7. MORSE STRIVES TO GET A PERFECT PICTURE: 1839

Letter, Samuel F. B. Morse to Louis J. M. Daguerre, November 16, 1839. Photostat from pencil draft, Morse Papers, Manuscript Div.

By the autumn of 1839 Morse was deep in experiments to produce a perfect daguerreotype. In this letter he asked Daguerre to send him two good lenses, and a sample of a daguerreotype for himself or the National Academy of Design. The brochure describing the process, which he read with "absorbing interest," undoubtedly was the *Historique et Description des Procédés du Daguerréotype*, published in 1839.

8. THE DAGUERREOTYPE PROCESS REVEALED TO THE PUBLIC: 1839

Louis-Jacques Mandé Daguerre, *Historique et Déscription des Procédés du Daguerréotype* . . . Paris, 1839.

SAMUEL F. B. MORSE, FATHER OF AMERICAN PHOTOGRAPHY; *75 years old.* *From a wet plate.* (See entry 3.)

The first report of Daguerre's discovery was made by his friend François Dominique Arago to the Royal French Academy of Sciences on January 7, 1839. The complete public report, delivered on August 19, was published in the Academy's proceedings. The *Historique et Description* has six illustrations of the apparatus, and was the first official description made accessible to the general public. At least 30 editions, in 8 languages, appeared in 1839 and 1840. Morse referred to it in his letter to Daguerre on November 16, 1839. (See entry 7.)

9. "THEIR EXQUISITE PERFECTION . . ."

Lewis Gaylord Clark, "The 'Daguerreotype' ", *The Knickerbocker* (New York), v. 14, p. 560, December 1839.

The enormous sensation aroused in the United States by daguerreotypy is shown by this article. His account was one of the first to popularize photography in this country. Clark saw some daguerreotypes in a shop window, and was so impressed that he wrote: "Their exquisite perfection almost transcends the bounds of sober belief."

10. SPREADING THE NEWS: 1839

Alexander Dallas Bache ("A. D. B."), "The Daguerreotype Explained," Franklin Institute *Journal*, v. 28, September 1839, page 209.

Scientific magazines played a major part in promoting American photography. One of the earliest notices of daguerreotypy appeared as this report of François Dominique Arago's discourse on the process (August 19, 1839). Bache, the noted American scientist, was a great-grandson of Benjamin Franklin, and president of the trustees of Girard College, Philadelphia.

11. ONE OF THE EARLIEST MANUALS OF DAGUERREOTYPY: 1841

"Buron," *Description de[s] Nouveaux Daguerréotypes Perfectionnés et Portatifs, avec L'Instruction de M. Daguerre, Annoté* [Paris] 1841.

This booklet describes the methods of obtaining proofs after a few seconds of exposure to light. The author was a Parisian manufacturer of optical and mathematical instruments, and the volume

was sold at optical stores in France and other countries.

12. EARLY TIME-EXPOSURE TABLE: 1840

A major problem of early photography was the length of exposure for taking exterior views. This table of rules, said to be the first one pub·lished in the United States, appeared in the March 1840 issue of the *American Repertory of Arts, Sciences, and Manufactures*, to illustrate a translation by J. S. Memes of Daguerre's original essay on his process.

13. INTERESTING EARLY USE OF PHOTOGRAPHY: 1841

Letter, Samuel F. B. Morse to Rev. Edward S. Salisbury, February 24, 1841. Photostat of page 3 of copy, Morse Papers, Manuscript Div.

Morse here describes his success in making daguerreotypes, achieved with considerable trouble and expense. Being a painter of portraits, he was interested in making use of the process to secure likenesses that could be transferred to canvas.

14. ONE OF THE FIRST AMERICAN DAGUERREOTYPE PORTRAITS: *ca.* DECEMBER 1839

Henry Fitz, Jr. (1808–63), self-portrait, showing him seated, with eyes closed. Exhibited by courtesy of the Smithsonian Institution.

Fitz, a native of Newburyport, Mass., worked in Boston and Cincinnati as a locksmith, and became well known as a maker of telescopes and lenses. He went to Europe in October 1839, and as soon as possible after his return took this picture, said to be the first successful camera portrait of a living person made in the United States. The plate was made with a hammer on a polished anvil. Fitz ran a daguerreotype studio in Baltimore.

15. SUSAN FITZ (1808–47)

Daguerreotype of Fitz's sister, *ca.* December 1839, probably made in his Baltimore studio. Exhibited by courtesy of the Smithsonian Institution.

AMBROTYPE OF NIAGARA FALLS, ca. *1854.* (See entry 19.)

16. SUSAN FITZ

Daguerreotype, probably made in Fitz's Baltimore studio. Exhibited by courtesy of the Smithsonian Institution.

17. PORTRAIT OF AN UNIDENTIFIED MAN

Undated daguerreotype by Fitz. Exhibited by courtesy of the Smithsonian Institution.

18. ONE OF THE EARLIEST AMERICAN SCENIC DAGUERREOTYPES: ca. 1840–44

A street scene in Baltimore, by Henry Fitz, Jr. Exhibited by courtesy of the Smithsonian Institution.

The early daguerreotype process was somewhat complicated, and difficult to perform outdoors. Views frequently were taken from the inside of a building—as when Samuel F. B. Morse took a daguerreotype of the Unitarian church in New York from a window of his studio.

19. AMBROTYPE OF NIAGARA FALLS: *ca.* 1854

The falls were one of the most challenging and popular subjects for the earlier photographers. While daguerreotypes were made on highly polished and sensitized metal, ambrotypes were made on glass plates. The elaborate case, with gilt frame and red velvet lining, is typical of the care used to protect the treasured pictures.

11

ONE OF THE EARLIEST AMERICAN CAMERAS, 1841. *Made by John Plumbe, Jr.* (See entry 25.)

Another view of the falls, reproduced from a daguerreotype, is displayed in the section entitled "Earliest Scenic Views, Nature and Cities." (See entry 102.)

LC–USZ62–10208

20. JENNY LIND, "THE SWEDISH NIGHT-INGALE": 1820–87

Daguerreotype, apparently taken during her tour of the United States, 1850–52.

Her début in opera at the age of 18 was a perfect triumph, and her tour of Europe in 1845 became an international sensation. In 1850 the famous showman, P. T. Barnum, brought her to the United States, and for about 2 years she toured the country, arousing excitement unprecedented for a singer. After her marriage at Boston in 1852, she returned to Europe and sang only for special occasions, her last public appearance being in 1870. LC–USZ62–8963

21. EMINENT AMERICAN JOURNALISTS OF THE MID-19TH CENTURY

The unknown artist who made this daguerreotype had the good fortune to "take" at once Horace Greeley, Charles A. Dana, and Bayard Taylor. Greeley edited the New York *Tribune* into a national institution. Dana for years was its managing editor, and later owned and edited the New York *Sun*, which he made famous for brilliant editorials. Taylor was a reporter for Greeley, and became nationally celebrated as a poet, author of books, lecturer on travel, and translator of German literature; and he also served as Ambassador to Germany.

LC–USZ62–8777

22. STEPHEN A. DOUGLAS (1813–61), "THE LITTLE GIANT"

Daguerreotype.

Douglas, a rival of Abraham Lincoln, was Congressman and Senator from Illinois, chairman of the Committee on Territories, and Northern Democratic candidate for President in 1860.

LC–USZ62–1754

23. PRESIDENT ABRAHAM LINCOLN AND HIS WIFE, MARY TODD LINCOLN

The original daguerreotypes from which these copies were made were received by the Library from the granddaughter of Abraham Lincoln, Mrs. Charles Isham. Lincoln was 38 years old when this portrait was made, according to information provided with the daguerreotype, which is the earliest known portrait of him. Both portraits were done about 1847, when Lincoln was serving in Washington as Representative from Illinois.

LC–USP6–2704A
LC–USP6–2706A

24. ORNAMENTAL "UNION CASES" FOR DAGUERREOTYPES: 1850's

Lent by courtesy of the George Eastman House.

While daguerreotypes were at the height of popularity, it was fashionable to protect them in a "Union Case" like these. Some cases were works of art, with delicate moldings, figured velvet linings, gilt frames, and tiny riveted and burnished hinges. Among the 12 displayed are examples from several companies that specialized in cases, notably the Scovill Manufacturing Co., Littlefield, Parsons & Co., Swain & Mead, and the Clifford Ambrotype Co. None of the portraits is identified.

25. ONE OF THE EARLIEST AMERICAN CAMERAS: 1841

Lent by courtesy of the George Eastman House. Made in Boston by John Plumbe, Jr. (1809–57).

Plumbe was a Welshman who became one of the best early American photographers. He learned daguerreotyping in 1840, and in the following year opened his Boston "Daguerreotype Depot," perhaps the first store for photographic materials in the United States. He established a series of daguerreotype galleries and became nationally famous. The camera, labeled "Manufactured at Plumbe's Daguerreotype Depot United States Photographic Institute, Boston," was made for quarter plates, and consists of two wooden telescoping boxes, the inner one to be slid for focusing and tightened by a screw, with a scale to measure the extent of the draw. A mirror reflector of ground glass is hinged to the bottom. The lens is incomplete, apparently the rear element of a doublet.

LC–USZ62–10995

26. DAGUERREOTYPE CAMERA OF 1848

Lent by courtesy of the George Eastman House.

This complete outfit is identical to the apparatus illustrated in Henry Hunt Snelling's instruction manual, *The History and Practice of the Art of Photography* (New York, 1849), and was made about the same time. The camera, for 6th-size plates (2¾ x 3¼ inches), consists of an outer wooden box veneered in mahogany, with double hinged doors at the top, and an inner box fitted with a frame to hold ground glass or a plateholder. The end is open to enable the operator to see the image on the ground glass. The doublet lens is in a brass mount, and has a focal length of 15 cm.

27. CAMERA TRIPOD

Lent by courtesy of the George Eastman House.

This device to support the daguerreotype camera has turned wooden legs, threaded to screw into a cast-iron fitting. The camera platform, adjustable by means of a wooden screw, is supported on a central wooden shaft.

28. PLATE VISE

Lent by courtesy of the George Eastman House.

Intended to hold the daguerreotype plate during the essential polishing operation: A wooden block, with a hook at one corner and a spring plunger at the diagonally opposite corner.

29. PLATEHOLDER

Lent by courtesy of the George Eastman House. From the daguerreotype gallery of Lucius H.

Cathan of Townshend, Vt. This one is similar, if not identical, to a model manufactured by Samuel Peck of New Haven, Conn. To use it the daguerreotypist bent over the diagonally opposite corner of the plate with pliers, and hooked it over the block.

30. BUFF STICK

Lent by courtesy of the George Eastman House.
Used for polishing daguerreotype plates: wood, covered with cotton and buckskin, protected by a scabbard made from a New York newspaper of 1848. The buff stick became the symbol of the daguerreotypist, because if the plate was not well polished with jeweler's rouge (a bottle of which is included in this outfit) he could not secure satisfactory results. To clean the stick when it was clogged with rouge, he used the brush displayed beside it.

31. COATING BOXES

Lent by courtesy of the George Eastman House.
These were used for sensitizing quarter-size daguerreotype plates (3¼ x 4¼ in.), and always in pairs. Inside the larger one is a glass jar for iodine particles used in the sensitizing process. The slide contains at one end a ground glass fitting tightly over the jar to keep the iodine from evaporating when not used. The other end contains a recessed aperture in which the polished plate was placed face down. The plate to be sensitized was slid over the jar. The smaller box contained "quickstuff," a bromine or chlorine or mixture of the two, and the plate was fumed first with iodine and then with "quickstuff."

32. MERCURY BATH

Lent by courtesy of the George Eastman House.
Used for developing ¼-size daguerreotype plates. Mercury was heated by an alcohol lamp in the cast-iron pot on an iron stand, and the plate was laid face down over the boiling liquid. A metal frame was supplied to allow the bath to be used for ⅙-size plates.

33. HEAD REST

Lent by courtesy of the George Eastman House.
Made of wood and cast iron, to be screwed to the back of a chair for use in taking portraits. The long exposure required for a daguerreotype made it necessary to "immobilize" the subject's head, and the instrument was therefore sometimes called an "immobilizer." This one, contrived especially for the convenience of traveling daguerreotypists, could be taken apart and closely packed.

34. ILLUSTRATIONS OF CAMERAS: 1854

In Henry Hunt Snelling, *A Dictionary of the Photographic Art*, New York, 1854. This is a complete encyclopedia of terms.

35. STEREOSCOPIC VIEWER, "BREWSTER TYPE": EARLY 1850's

Manufactured by the American Stereoscopic Co. for Frederick and William Langenheim of Philadelphia. Lent by courtesy of Beaumont Newhall.
The Langenheim brothers commercially introduced into the United States stereoscopic views produced by the camera, and began to make them extensively in 1854–55. For a long time the stereoscopic view was the most popular form of photography, especially for scenery. This viewer consists of a tapered box with a lens at the back protected by hinged doors. The top opens for insertion of the stereo slide.

36. STEREOSCOPIC VIEWER, "HOLMES TYPE"

Lent by courtesy of the George Eastman House.
Probably made in the 1850's, when the stereoscopic view became popular. This one is on a stand, and bears the trademark "American Lens Stereoscope."

37. MAGAZINE STEREOSCOPIC VIEWER

Lent by courtesy of the George Eastman House.
Patented by L. A. Beckers.
This type contains holders for 100 cards (50 back to back) on an endless belt operated by

knobs at either side, and it has hinged tops to be raised to permit reflected light to illuminate the cards, upon which two pairs of lenses are focused. Two persons could view at the same time.

Pioneers and Their Work and Records

38. JOHN W. DRAPER (1811–82), PHOTOGRAPHIC SCIENTIST: 1860

Photograph, frontispiece to *American Journal of Photography*, new series, v. 3, No. 15, January 1, 1861.

Closely associated with Samuel F. B. Morse, Draper was the friend and teacher of Mathew B. Brady, and one of the first Americans to test Daguerre's process.

39. YOUNG MASTER OF THE DAGUERREOTYPE: 1851

Photograph from lithograph by F. D'Avignon, from a daguerreotype of 1845, frontispiece to *Photographic Art Journal*, v. 1, 1851, with an article, "M. B. Brady and the Photographic Art," by C. Edwards Lester, the art critic.

This is thought to be the first portrait of Mathew B. Brady, the farm boy from Warren County, N. Y., who at the age of 28 was already the Nation's leading photographer.

LC–USZ62–10991

40. BRADY'S FIRST EMPLOYER IN NEW YORK

Alexander T. Stewart. From a wet plate by Brady or an assistant, *ca.* 1856.

The merchant prince hired Brady as a clerk in his store when the latter came to New York in 1839–40. Brady recently had met the portrait artist William Page, for whom he copied sketches, and shortly went with him to the big city. Page introduced him to S. F. B. Morse, from whom Brady learned daguerreotypy while working at Stewart's. In 1844 he opened his own gallery

and won a silver medal at the first competitive photographic exhibition.   LC–BH82–4785

41. BRADY'S FIRST AWARD: 1844

Photograph of certificate, the highest award of the American Institute, conferred upon Brady in his first year as a professional daguerreotypist.

LC–BH838–83

42. BRADY'S NEW YORK GALLERY: 1861

"M. B. Brady's New Photographic Gallery, Corner of Broadway and Tenth Street." Photostat of engraving in *Frank Leslie's Illustrated Newspaper* for January 5, 1861, page 108.

Brady opened the gallery in 1860 to accommodate the huge expansion of his business and transferred to it his unrivaled collection of historical photographs. The sheer size and ornate decoration reveal his prosperity, and the growth of photography into a big business in only 20 years.

43. BRADY AND HIS WIFE

From a daguerreotype.

After an unsuccessful attempt nine years earlier, Brady in 1858 opened a studio in Washington, the mecca of the Nation's great and near-great personalities. There he was married to Juliet Elizabeth ("Julia") Handy, the daughter of a Maryland lawyer, Col. Samuel Handy, who had come to the Washington studio for his portrait. This daguerreotype, made about the time of the marriage, shows the couple with Mrs. Haggarty, a relative. The Bradys lived at the famous old National Hotel on Pennsylvania Avenue.

LC–BH8331–582

44. PAGES FROM BRADY'S WASHINGTON REGISTER: 1870–73

Photostat of 2 pages.

For many years after the Civil War Brady conducted his "National Portrait Gallery," at 494 Maryland Avenue SW., together with Levin C. Handy, the son of his wife's brother. These pages record the names of many famous persons who sat for portraits.

45. ALEXANDER GARDNER'S GALLERY IN WASHINGTON: 1865

The gallery was established by one of Brady's famous group of assistants. Alexander Gardner became one of the greatest American photographers of the mid-nineteenth century. He was a Scottish scientist and journalist, who mastered photography and in 1856 came to America to join Brady, who appointed him as manager of his Washington studio. Gardner later opened his own gallery at 7th and D Streets NW., and recorded Civil War and western frontier scenes.

LC–BH837–207

46. PHOTOGRAPHY INVADES THE WEST

"Ball's Great Daguerrian Gallery of the West," Cincinnati, Ohio. Photostat of engraving, *Gleason's Pictorial*, Boston, April 1, 1854, page 208.

The popularity of the "new art" spread across the United States with almost explosive speed, and within a few years daguerreotype artists were opening studios almost on the frontier. Cincinnati became a photographic center, and one of the leading establishments was Ball's gallery. It was described in *Gleason's Pictorial*, with an engraving showing a typically overdecorated daguerreotype "parlor."

47. A WESTERN SMALL-TOWN PHOTOGRAPHER: *ca.* 1865

Portrait of Isaac Augustus Wetherby (1819–1904), from one of his early glass plates.

Many now almost forgotten photographers flourished in the West during the first period of the art in America. One of these was Wetherby, who made many portraits in New England but in 1859 went to Iowa and settled in Iowa City. This portrait shows him in his studio.

LC–USZ62–3529

48. WETHERBY STUDIO, IOWA CITY: 1865

Copy from one of his early glass plates, showing the interior of his studio on Clinton Street.

On the walls are some of his portraits, including one of an Indian. The typical photographic gallery of the time was as elaborately decorated as the owner could afford, and adorned with closely hung samples of his work, to be admired while the clients waited. LC–USZ62–3549

49. GEORGE S. COOK, PHOTOGRAPHER OF THE OLD SOUTH: 1851

Lithograph by F. D'Avignon, New York, frontispiece to *Photographic Art Journal*, v. 1, No. 5, May 1851.

After unsuccessfully trying mercantile business, Cook went to New Orleans, where he became a painter. He was attracted to daguerreotypy when visiting a gallery run by some friends. He took charge of their establishment, and before long was the best at the art in town. He toured several Southern States, establishing galleries and teaching many pupils, and about 1851 settled in Charleston, S. C. He was noted especially for his skill in lighting, and in tinting daguerreotypes.

50. CONFEDERATE PHOTOGRAPHER'S ACCOUNT BOOK: 1863–64

Photostats of 4 pages in the account book of George S. Cook of Charleston, S. C. From the Cook Papers, Manuscript Div.

These show how busy Cook was, even in the midst of the trials of the Civil War. Notations illustrate the variety of his work, and of the people who sat for portraits. One entry is for sale of carte-de-visite photographs of General Beauregard. Cook, who had been in charge of Mathew B. Brady's gallery in 1851, became one of the more prominent Confederate Civil War photographers.

51. GROWING USE OF PHOTOGRAPHY IN THE NEWS: 1861

Letter, Walter Dinmore & Co. Gallery, Philadelphia, to George S. Cook, Charleston, S. C., January 11, 1861. Photostat from Cook Papers, Manuscript Div.

About the time of the Civil War there was a vogue for card photographs of eminent people. One of the first celebrities to be exploited was Maj. Robert Anderson, the Union commander of Fort Sumter. After George S. Cook of Charleston had photographed him, the Anthony brothers bought the negatives and made 1,000 prints a day. In this letter the Walter Dinmore Gallery of Philadelphia tries to make a deal with Cook to "cash in" on Anderson's popularity and split the profits.

The Nation's Capital, 1840-1869

52. THE CAPITAL CITY IN PRESIDENT TYLER'S TIME: 1843

This copy of a rare daguerreotype certainly is one of the earliest photographic views of Washington, D. C. It was taken when John Tyler was President, and before Mathew B. Brady had opened his Washington branch gallery. It shows Pennsylvania Avenue looking west from the Capitol toward the White House, and includes the famous Metropolitan Hotel. Many of the daguerreotypes were reversed, and therefore this print has been reversed, so that the buildings are seen in their correct positions. LC–BH837–203

53. THE CAPITOL WITHOUT ITS DOME: ca. 1858

From a wet plate by Mathew B. Brady or an assistant, taken from the rear (west) in President Buchanan's administration. The dome was completed in the following decade. The old greenhouse and the practically disused canal to the Navy Yard appear in the foreground.
LC–BH837–205

54. EARLY PHOTOGRAPH OF THE WHITE HOUSE

Although it is undated, this is believed by some authorities to be the earliest photographic view of the President's house, and to have been made possibly by Mathew B. Brady. This is the north front, facing Pennsylvania Avenue.
LC–BH835–16

55. DOLLEY MADISON, WASHINGTON HOSTESS: 1768-1849

From a daguerreotype by Mathew B. Brady. Political circles had practically given up James Madison as an incorrigible bachelor when, at the age of 45, he married the charming and lively Dolley Todd. She made his Presidency (1809–17) a social success, and brightened his retirement on his estate of "Montpelier," near Orange, Va. During a long widowhood she remained a favorite in Washington society. LC–BH834–35

56. OLD TRINITY CHURCH, WASHINGTON

The church formerly stood at Third Street and Indiana Avenue NW., and in the mid-nineteenth century was attended by many social and political leaders. It was torn down in the late 1930's and the site is now a parking lot. In the background is seen the unfinished Capitol. LC–BH823–1

57. ENLARGING THE CAPITOL: EARLY 1860's

From a wet plate made by Mathew B. Brady or one of his assistants. It shows one of the great wings nearing completion. LC–BH8234–112

58. GEORGETOWN AQUEDUCT BRIDGE: ca. 1862

By George N. Barnard, assistant to Mathew B. Brady, and later official photographer to the Engineer Corp. The view from the Georgetown side of the Potomac River shows the old Chesapeake & Ohio Canal (still extant) in the foreground. The aqueduct was built in 1838, during the days of "canal fever" in investment, to provide a direct canal barge connection to Alexandria. Early in the Civil War the Army altered the aqueduct into a bridge to provide another river crossing for the defense of Washington.
LC–USZ62–4570

59. GEORGETOWN SEEN FROM THE RIVER: 1865

By William M. Smith. Georgetown's character as a port is indicated by the ships tied up just below the Aqueduct Bridge. The high trestles behind them, at the level of the Chesapeake & Ohio Canal, were used to move material from the canal barges to sailing vessels.
LC–B8184–7894

60. SECURITY CHECK IN WARTIME: 1861-62

Photograph by George N. Barnard, one of Mathew B. Brady's assistants, showing a guard examining a pass at the Georgetown ferry. Barnard later made photographs with General Sherman's army in Georgia, and became the

18

OLD TRINITY CHURCH, WASHINGTON, D. C. *Unfinished Capitol in the background.* (See entry 56.)

official photographer for the Engineer Corps; he took a number of shots of the defenses of the city. LC–USZ62–4571

61. WOUNDED MEN IN THE ARMORY SQUARE HOSPITAL: 1861–65

By Mathew B. Brady or one of his staff. This is Ward K, in one of the temporary buildings erected on the grounds during the Civil War. To this ward came Walt Whitman, to help care for the wounded. The armory was erected in 1855 on the Mall east of Seventh Street, for the use of the District of Columbia militia and as a military museum. LC–USZ62–4573

62. BEEF FOR THE ARMY: APRIL 1865

By Mathew B. Brady or one of his staff. The cattle were pastured on the Mall, south of the Treasury Building, and the slaughterhouses were near the Washington Monument. Throughout the Civil War Washington was a vast military depot, with acres of supplies to equip and feed the Army, and huge corrals for horses and mules. LC–USZ62–4501

63. "THE AVENUE": ca. 1865

Even after the Civil War Washington's principal street retained much of its earlier appearance, the only improvement being the horsecar railway which was laid from the Capitol to Georgetown in 1862. As Pennsylvania Avenue was Federal property, it could be improved only by Congressional action, and the city could not restrain stray animals like the lone horse in the foreground. LC–USZ62–4529

64. THE OLD LIBRARY OF CONGRESS: 1867

From 2 stereographic photographs by Bell and Brothers, indicating the crowded condition of the Library when it was housed on the main floor west in the central section of the Capitol. Adjoining the reading room was an equally crowded working space for the staff. Such conditions led to the erection of the present Main Building of the Library in the 1890's. LC–USZ62–4495, 4496

65. DEPARTMENT OF AGRICULTURE BUILDING: 1869

From a stereographic photograph by Bell and Brothers. The Department of Agriculture was authorized in 1862, and for many years was quartered in this Renaissance-style building on the Mall at 14th Street, the site of the present North Agriculture Building. LC–USZ62–4601

66. INAUGURATION OF PRESIDENT ULYSSES S. GRANT: MARCH 4, 1869

By Mathew B. Brady or one of his staff, showing part of the crowd. The great Civil War general was inaugurated on a day of cloudy skies and showers. LC–USZ62–4583

Early Portraits of Presidents, 1840-1869

67. JOHN QUINCY ADAMS, "THE OLD MAN ELOQUENT": 1825–29

From a daguerreotype, taken in the 1840's.
Mr. Adams' experiences with photography were not always happy, and he once described some daguerreotypes of him as "all hideous." This one turned out well and depicts him in the mid-1840's, when he was serving in Congress as a Representative from Massachusetts and eloquently defending the right to present antislavery petitions. He was the only ex-President ever to serve in the House of Representatives.
LC–BH82–5159

68. ANDREW JACKSON, "OLD HICKORY": 1829–37

India ink copy of a daguerreotype.
Jackson's nickname is suggested by the rugged, lined, determined countenance. The daguerreotype is said to have been made just before his death at the "Hermitage," his Tennessee home, in 1845. Marquis James, in his biography of Jackson, relates a tradition that Brady transported his equipment there and made the picture on

April 15, 1845. Late in life Mathew B. Brady said in an interview that he "sent" to have the portrait made. LC–BH8331–202

69. MARTIN VAN BUREN, "THE LITTLE MAGICIAN": 1837–41

From a daguerreotype by Mathew B. Brady.

Van Buren's innumerable friends among the people gave him the title out of respect for his legendary political adroitness. Later times have acknowledged his abilities as a statesman and diplomat, and as the chief adviser of President Jackson. History now credits him with the courage to advocate sound financial policy, and to take the unpopular course, as when he became the Free-Soil candidate for President in 1848. LC–BH834–6

70. JOHN TYLER, "PRESIDENT WITHOUT A PARTY": 1841–45

From a daguerreotype by Mathew B. Brady, taken probably in 1845.

Largely because his independence estranged him from strict party men, Tyler was generally underrated and has been forgotten by most Americans. But he was among the ablest of the brilliant line of Virginia statesmen who served the Nation, in his case as State legislator, Federal judge, Governor, Congressman, Senator, and Vice President. He was the first Vice President to succeed upon the death of a President (William Henry Harrison). LC–BH8277–523

71. BRADY PHOTOGRAPHS A DYING PRESIDENT: 1849

Photostat of page in President James K. Polk's diary, February 14, 1849, recording the visit of Mathew B. Brady to the White House to make a daguerreotype of him. From the Polk Papers, Manuscript Div.

Brady asked the President where he could get the best light, and Polk led him to the large dining room.

72. JAMES K. POLK, "YOUNG HICKORY": 1845–49

From the Brady daguerreotype mentioned in Polk's diary (See entry 71).

The President was already sinking under the disease that claimed his life only a few months after he left the White House. History now knows him well as a forceful leader of the Democratic Party in Congress, as an able Governor of Tennessee, and as the statesman President whose administration passed many vital laws and added 1,000,000 square miles to our territory. LC–BH82–8

73. ZACHARY TAYLOR, "OLD ROUGH AND READY": 1849–50

From a daguerreotype by Mathew B. Brady, 1849.

Taylor won this title of affection and admiration from the soldiers during his long and rugged service in the Army, in which he really earned the rank of brigadier general. His decisive victory at Buena Vista in the Mexican War made him the Whig candidate for President in 1848. This is said to be the first published photograph of a President and his Cabinet. Taylor was the second President to die in office, in 1850. LC–USZ62–10985

74. MILLARD FILLMORE, PEACEMAKER: 1850–53

From a negative by Mathew B. Brady.

Fillmore's succession to the Presidency, upon Taylor's death in 1850, crowned a long career in the New York Legislature, and as Congressman and Vice President. Long obscured by more brilliant contemporary statesmen, the gracious Fillmore has gradually attained recognition for his efforts to soothe the violent and disruptive slavery controversy in 1850, and for his contributions to many civic, educational, and philanthropic enterprises. LC–BH82–7

75. FRANKLIN PIERCE, CONCILIATOR: 1853–57

From a daguerreotype.

It was the fate of this winning and peace-loving man to be President in the bitter and violent 1850's, when the slavery controversy was rending the Nation. His failure to make peace has clouded his previous creditable service in the New

PRESIDENT JOHN QUINCY ADAMS. *From a daguerreotype, 1840's.* (See entry 67.)

Hampshire Legislature, and as Congressman and Senator. He enjoyed the distinction of having his biography written by a literary genius, his lifelong friend and Bowdoin College classmate, Nathaniel Hawthorne.   LC–USZ62–9059

76. PRESIDENT JAMES BUCHANAN AND HIS CABINET: *ca.* 1859

From a·daguerreotype by Mathew B. Brady.

Few American statesmen of any period have enjoyed such a varied and useful career as he, in his nearly half a century of service as legislator, political leader, diplomat, Secretary of State, and President. Mathew B. Brady made the daguerreotype from which this photograph was taken. Left to right, seated: Jacob Thompson, Interior; John B. Floyd, War; Isaac Toucey, Navy; Jeremiah S. Black, Attorney General; standing: Lewis Cass, State; President Buchanan; Howell Cobb, Treasury; Joseph Holt, Postmaster General.   LC–BH8277–537

77. ANDREW JOHNSON: SOUTHERN UNIONIST: 1865–69

By Mathew B. Brady's Washington (D. C.) Gallery, 1865.

This undoubtedly is the portrait which Johnson had made in response to Brady's urgent plea (See entry 78). It reveals the rugged courage and tenacity that inspired his rise to the Nation's highest office, and made him work for the Union cause in Tennessee in 1861 at the risk of his life. After retirement from the Presidency, he was elected Senator from Tennessee in 1875—the only instance of an ex-President so chosen.   LC–BH83–171

78. BRADY ASKS THE TAILOR PRESIDENT TO SIT: 1865

Photostat of letter (not in Brady's handwriting) from Brady's Gallery to Vice President Andrew Johnson. From the Johnson Papers, Manuscript Div.

Andrew Johnson's startling rise from the tailor's bench to the Vice Presidency and the White House was a remarkable success story. In this letter Mathew B. Brady requests Johnson,

on the eve of his inauguration as Vice President, to favor him with a sitting in order to satisfy the clamor for his picture. Within a few weeks, by the assassination of Lincoln, Johnson became President.

Pre-Civil War Statesmen and Politicians

79. ALBERT GALLATIN, DEMOCRATIC FINANCIER: 1761–1849

From a daguerreotype.

This Swiss-born merchant and mathematician brought to the United States an unusual combination of talents as statesman, diplomat, and financier. He became the financial expert of the Jeffersonian Party, and served as Secretary of the Treasury under Presidents Jefferson and Madison, 1801–13.   LC–USZ62–10986

80. THE ELOQUENT HENRY CLAY: 1777–1852

From a daguerreotype by Mathew B. Brady.

For nearly half a century the great Kentucky Senator and Secretary of State was a legendary figure to Americans. He will always be famous as an orator, and as the author of the "American System" of protective tariff, internal improvements, and a national bank; also of the great compromise measures that saved the Nation from violent sectional strife in 1820, 1833, and 1850.   LC–BH8277–551

81. STEPHEN A. DOUGLAS, THE "LITTLE GIANT": 1813–61

From a daguerreotype by Mathew B. Brady.

Douglas learned the trade of cabinetmaking as a boy in Vermont, and became a political cabinetmaker in his adopted State of Illinois, which sent him to the United States Senate. As chairman of the Committee on Territories he powerfully aided settlement and development of the West.   LC–BH834–14

HENRY CLAY. *From a daguerreotype by Brady.* (See entry 80.)

82. VICE PRESIDENT WILLIAM R. KING: 1786–1853

From a daguerreotype.

King has become one of the nearly forgotten statesmen of the early nineteenth century. After a brief career as lawyer and legislator in his native North Carolina, King moved to Alabama, where he helped to draft the new State's constitution and became one of its first two United States Senators. He was Minister to France in 1844–46, presided over the Senate in the Presidency of Millard Fillmore, and in 1853 became Vice President under Franklin Pierce.

LC–USZ62–10668

83. "PRINCE JOHN" VAN BUREN: 1810–66

From a daguerreotype.

This once-famous lawyer and politician was the son of President Martin Van Buren. He aided his father in political campaigns, especially in 1848 as a Free Soil orator. The British liked him as a young legation attaché when his father was American Minister, and the New York Bar long remembered his ability as a jury lawyer and his service as the State's attorney general.

LC–USZ62–10990

84. JOHN M. CLAYTON, EMINENT STATESMAN: 1796–1856

From a daguerreotype.

Clayton was one of several highly respected public servants in the early nineteenth century who came from the little State of Delaware, where public service was a tradition in the old aristocratic families. He was Chief Justice of Delaware and United States Senator, and became Secretary of State for President Taylor, 1849–50.

LC–USZ62–9053

85. DANIEL WEBSTER, THE GREAT ORATOR: 1782–1852

From a daguerreotype by Mathew B. Brady, made for a lithograph by D'Avignon in Brady's *The Gallery of Illustrious Americans*, 1850.

Webster rose from a New Hampshire farm and Dartmouth College to be the great orator of American liberty and union. He was already a noted lawyer and speaker before he began his long public career as Congressman, Senator, and Secretary of State. His occasional patriotic orations, and his speeches in Congress, implanted in the people a deep devotion to the Union that helped to save it in the crisis of the Civil War.

LC–BH834–11

86. THOMAS HART ("OLD BULLION") BENTON: 1782–1858

From a daguerreotype by Mathew B. Brady.

The half-humorous sobriquet originated from Benton's zealous advocacy of a purely metallic currency. As Senator from Missouri for 30 years (1820–50) Thomas Hart Benton fearlessly championed Jacksonian democracy, favored development of the West, defended the Union, and was nationally famous as an orator and debater with very few equals. Near the close of his life he wrote his *Thirty Years' View*, one of the greatest American political autobiographies.

LC–BH8277–540

87. SAM HOUSTON, PRESIDENT OF TEXAS: 1793–1863

From a daguerreotype by Mathew B. Brady.

Houston was a Virginian who adopted Tennessee as his State, and was adopted by an Indian chief. Into one life he compressed various lives as teacher, lawyer, frontier fighter, general of militia, Governor, Congressman, commander of the army in the Texan war for independence, and Senator from Texas. His powerful eloquence became a national legend, and his loyalty to the Union in 1861 crowned his heroic life.

LC–USZ62–9051

Other Pre-Civil War Celebrities

88. CYRUS FIELD, OCEAN TELEGRAPH PROMOTER: 1819–92

From a daguerreotype.

Field came to New York City from the Berkshire Hills of Massachusetts and became a merchant prince. Impressed by the long delays of commercial communication across the Atlantic, he organized a company to lay telegraph cables on the ocean floor. Undismayed by ridicule and repeated failures, he succeeded at last in 1866 with a cable laid by the steamer *Great Eastern*.

LC–USZ62–9055

89. THE FABULOUS P. T. BARNUM: 1810–91

From a daguerreotype by Mathew B. Brady.

This smart Connecticut Yankee early displayed the traits of a born advertiser, trader, joker, and showman. He began his swift ascent to world-wide notoriety in 1841 by buying a New York museum, which he speedily made the Nation's most popular amusement place. He was the showman of General Tom Thumb and of Jenny Lind the singer, started a circus, and wrote a rousing autobiography. LC–BH82–4961

90. AUGUST BELMONT, FINANCIER: 1816–90

From a daguerreotype.

The founder of a banking dynasty, Belmont learned the business from the Rothschilds in his native Germany and represented them in New York. His public career comprised diplomatic service for the United States in Austria and Holland (1844–58), and 12 years (1860–72) as chairman of the Democratic National Committee.

LC–USZ62–9058

91. CORNELIUS VANDERBILT, CAPITALIST: 1794–1872

From a daguerreotype.

People called Vanderbilt "Corny" and "the Commodore," but respectfully and sometimes fearfully. From the humble place of captain of a ferryboat plying between New York City and his native Staten Island, he rose swiftly to the control of river, harbor, and ocean steamships. Later shifting to railroad finance and management, he ran the New York Central lines, founded Vanderbilt University in Tennessee, and died with a fortune of around $100,000,000.

LC–USZ62–10976

92. BRIGHAM YOUNG, LEADER OF AN AMERICAN RELIGION: 1801–77

From a daguerreotype, possibly by Mathew B. Brady.

Young is known chiefly as the president of the Church of Jesus Christ of Latter-Day Saints (Mormons) from 1847 to 1877. After leading his people overland to Utah, he served as Governor of the Territory, and became also a leader in development of the West by encouraging irrigation, railroads, the telegraph, and the founding of the University of Utah. LC–BH82–875

93. PHILANDER CHASE, BACKWOODS BISHOP: 1775–1852

From a daguerreotype.

The first Bishop of Ohio (1819), and the first of the Episcopal Church west of the Alleghenies, Chase was a typical frontier missionary. He twice visited England to seek help for his missions and for the two colleges he founded in Ohio and Illinois, and excited great curiosity as a bishop who had ridden horseback on forest trails, lived in a log house, and done his own farming. For the last 9 years of his life he was presiding bishop of the Episcopal Church.

LC–USZ62–10989

94. FATHER DE SMET, FRIEND OF THE INDIAN: 1801–73

From a daguerreotype by Mathew B. Brady.

Pierre Jean De Smet came to the United States from Belgium in 1822, and spent the next 50 years as a teacher and missionary to the far western Indians. In 40 years he traveled over 180,000 miles, acting as a peacemaker among wild tribes which no other white man could safely approach. He found time to make several visits to Europe for aid, and to write entertaining narratives of his adventures. LC–BH824–5343

95. "STONEWALL" JACKSON: 1824–63

From a daguerreotype taken probably during the Mexican War, possibly by Mathew B. Brady, shortly after Jackson's graduation from the Military Academy at West Point.

Thomas Jonathan Jackson won his nickname for his steadfastness at the First Battle of Bull

Run, became a general in the Confederate Army, and was a heroic figure loved and respected by both sides. LC–BH8331–569

96. JOHN C. FRÉMONT, "PATHFINDER OF THE ROCKIES": 1813–90

From a daguerreotype by Mathew B. Brady or an assistant.

Frémont began his career as a civil engineer engaged in railroad route surveying. Between 1842 and 1853 he led five exploring expeditions into the almost unknown trans-Mississippi West, and took a prominent part in the acquisition of California. He was one of the first Senators from California, the first Republican candidate for President in 1856, a Union general in the Civil War, a railroad promoter, Governor of Arizona (1878–81), and author of books on exploration and travel and of an entertaining autobiography. LC–BH82–523

97. HORACE MANN, CHAMPION OF GOOD PUBLIC SCHOOLS: 1796–1859

From a daguerreotype.

Mann's early career was devoted to the practice of law and service in the Massachusetts Legislature, and his significant contribution to American life began with his appointment as secretary of the Massachusetts Board of Education. In 11 years, against bitter opposition, he covered the State with modern schoolhouses and transformed teaching methods. His reports and lectures inspired unprecedented interest in better education. LC–USZ62–10988

98. JOSEPH STORY, TEACHER OF LAW: 1779–1845

From a daguerreotype.

When he became an Associate Justice of the Supreme Court of the United States at 32, Story was one of the youngest men ever appointed to that position. He already had behind him a bright career as a legislator in Massachusetts and in Congress, and he soon became the friend and disciple of Chief Justice Marshall in stressing the just powers of the Federal Government. He became professor of law at Harvard and wrote legal works that are still consulted. LC–USZ62–10984

99. THE PRINCE OF WALES IN BRADY'S GALLERY: 1860

From a daguerreotype made in October 1860 in Brady's Tenth Street Gallery, New York.

The Prince is in the center; second from left is Lord Lyons, British Minister in Washington, 1858–65. LC–BH82–6

100. THE PRINCE OF WALES LEAVING THE UNITED STATES: 1860

From one of Stacy's "American Stereoscopic Views."

The Prince (later King Edward VII, 1901–10) is shown at Portland, Maine, with Mayor Howard (on his left), just before he sailed for England on October 20. In front (left) is Lord Lyons, British Minister to the United States during the Civil War. LC–USZ62–10996

Earliest Scenic Views, Nature and Cities

101. SAN FRANCISCO HARBOR IN THE GOLD RUSH: 1852–53

Photocopies of five daguerreotypes, by William Shew, from a panoramic view. Lent by courtesy of the Smithsonian Institution.

The harbor is full of ships deserted by their crews, who had fled to the hills to seek for gold. This is undoubtedly one of the earliest photographs ever taken of the Golden Gate City.

102. NIAGARA FALLS: *ca.* 1854

Photograph from a daguerreotype, probably by Platt D. Babbitt.

The falls were one of the most challenging and popular subjects for the earlier daguerreotypists. LC–USZ62–9063

VIEWS OF PHILADELPHIA: 1856

These three views were reproduced from stereographs made by the brothers Frederick and William Langenheim. They are believed to have been the first American photographers to produce stereographs on a commercial scale. The prints, which were made from proofs on salted paper, are in an album entitled "Photographic Views at Home and Abroad Taken and Published by F. Langenheim, 188 Chestnut Street, Philadelphia, 1856."

103. PHILADELPHIA FROM THE STEEPLE OF INDEPENDENCE HALL, LOOKING NORTH: 1856   LC–USZ62–10982

104. PHILADELPHIA FROM THE STEEPLE OF INDEPENDENCE HALL, LOOKING NORTHWEST: 1856
LC–USZ62–10980

105. PHILADELPHIA FROM THE STEEPLE OF INDEPENDENCE HALL, LOOKING WEST: 1856   LC–USZ62–10981

VIEWS OF "LITTLE OLD NEW YORK": 1856

These two views were reproduced from stereographs made by the brothers Frederick and William Langenheim. These prints, which were made from proofs on salted paper, are in an album entitled "Photographic Views at Home and Abroad Taken and Published by F. Langenheim, 188 Chestnut Street, Philadelphia, 1856."

106. WALL STREET, NEW YORK, FROM TRINITY CHURCH: *ca.* 1856
LC–USZ62–10979

PHOTOGRAPHERS OF THE MAMMOTH CAVE, KY., 1866. *From a stereograph.* (See entry 110.)

107. BROADWAY, NEW YORK, FROM BARNUM'S MUSEUM: *ca.* 1856
LC–USZ62–10978

108. THE OLD MARKET IN PHILADELPHIA: 1859

From a stereoscopic view, made probably in 1859 by H. B. Odiorne, comprising the range of the "Market Houses" from 8th to Front Street.
LC–USZ62–10983

109. AN INDIAN VILLAGE

Photograph reproduced from an undated but undoubtedly early daguerreotype.
LC–USZ62–9065

EARLY PHOTOGRAPHS IN KENTUCKY'S MAMMOTH CAVE: 1866

These four views are copies of stereographs made by magnesium light by Charles Waldack of Cincinnati, Ohio. They were probably the first subterranean photographs made in the United States, and were published by E. and H. T. Anthony & Co., New York photographers. The prints in the Library of Congress are copyright deposits, dated 1866.

110. "NO. 4. OUT FOR THE LAST TIME"

"This is a picture of the gentlemen who conceived and executed the project of photographing the cave, with the reflectors, &c. used."
LC–USZ62–11004

111. "NO. 6. MOUTH OF THE CAVE . . ."

"This view introduces three well-known guides. The one on the right is old 'Mat,' who has acted in the capacity of guide for the last thirty years."
LC–USZ62–11003

112. ENTRANCE TO FAT MAN'S MISERY FROM GREAT RELIEF
LC–USZ62–11002

113. ECHO RIVER

"Echo River is about ten to thirty feet deep. It is generally traveled about three-quarters of a mile."
LC–USZ62–11001

Part Two: 1869-1900

Exploring the Continent

114. DOWN THE GRAND CANYON WITH A CAMERA: 1871

By E. O. Beaman, 1871, for Maj. John Wesley Powell's United States Topographical and Geological Survey of the Colorado of the West.

The party is shown in camp, with photographic equipment. Powell led several surveys of the region in 1869-78; Beaman accompanied the second expedition in 1871, and learned the art of photography amid hardships in the wilderness. LC–USZ62–10906

115. MUMMY CAVE, CAÑON DEL MUERTE, ARIZONA: ca. 1873

Original print by John K. Hillers, for the Survey of the Colorado of the West.

Hillers was official photographer for the survey in 1872-76 and 1878, and on his first expedition learned photography from the beginning, in spite of almost incredible difficulties and fatigue. His work was made famous by *Canyon Voyage*, written by Frederick S. Dellenbaugh, his companion on the expedition of 1871. LC–USZ62–23

116. BLACK CAÑON OF THE COLORADO: 1871

Original print by Timothy H. O'Sullivan, for Lt. George M. Wheeler's Geographical Explorations and Surveys West of the 100th Meridian.

Looking upstream from one of the camps, showing one of the expedition's boats, containing O'Sullivan's tiny darkroom and a member of the party. William Henry Jackson, himself a renowned photographer of the West, knew O'Sullivan well and praised him as "one of the best of the Government photographers." LC–USZ62–11056

117. AMERICAN EXPLORER'S CAMP IN THE ARCTIC: 1864

By Messrs. Dunmore and Critcherson, studio of J. W. Black, Boston, on an expedition to Labrador directed by William Bradford (1823-92) of New Bedford, Mass.

Bradford, a well-known marine painter, chartered a vessel, and in Eskimo dress made a detailed study of icebergs and floes as a basis for paintings. The studio of Black, a noted Boston photographer, in 1860 collaborated with Samuel A. King of Providence to photograph Boston from a balloon. (See entry 334.) LC–USZ62–11013

118. ESKIMO IN HIS KAYAK: 1864

By Messrs. Dunmore and Critcherson, studio of J. W. Black, Boston, on the Bradford expedition to Labrador in 1864, to study Arctic ice formations.

The photographs eventually were bound into an album of albumen prints, which was presented to the Library of Congress by Mr. Copley Amory in 1942. LC–USZ62–11043

119. SHIP OF THE GREELY ARCTIC EXPEDITION: 1881-84

Proteus at Cape Hawkes, August [1881], by Sgt. George W. Rice, photographer of the Lady Franklin Bay Expedition, and of the rescue expedition of 1884.

The *Proteus* was specially built for Arctic service, and was manned by Newfoundland fishermen. The expedition, led voluntarily by Adolphus W. Greely (1844-1935) of the United States Army, proposed to establish stations to study Arctic weather and climate. Greely served later in the regular United States Army Signal Corps. LC–USZ62–11026

DOWN THE GRAND CANYON WITH A CAMERA, 1871. *E. O. Beaman and party.* (See entry 114.)

BLACK CAÑON, COLORADO RIVER, 1871. *Timothy H. O'Sullivan's darkroom.* (See entry 116.)

120. KAYAKS AND NATIVES AT PROVEN, GREENLAND: JULY 1881

By Sgt. George W. Rice.

This picture, taken in the first summer of the expedition, shows an old type of Eskimo life that has practically disappeared. Most of the party perished, because no relief expedition came until the summer of 1884. Greely described the adventure in his *Three Years of Arctic Service*, and on his 91st birthday received the Congressional Medal of Honor. LC–USZ62–10905

121. HAULING ICE AT CONGER

Lieutenant Greely is the third from the left.
LC–USZ62–11017

Old West and Frontier

122. OREGON CELEBRATES ADMISSION AS A STATE: 1859

Copy print, photographer unidentified. From the McClain Collection of early Oregon photographs.

Taken on June 22, 1859, this photograph shows the celebration in Portland, with a parade featuring a band and oldtime fire apparatus. The State constitution was drafted by a convention at Salem in August and September 1857, and was ratified by popular vote in November. The act for admission was approved by President James Buchanan on February 14, 1859.

123. A TYPICAL CALIFORNIA MINING CLAIM: 1859

Sardine Claim. Copy of an album print, from a photograph by E. P. Vollum, a physician of the United States Army who was stationed in California. From the Vollum Collection of Gold Rush photographs.

Typical features of the scene are the sluices and water wheels, and the frame building being hastily erected on a hillside, in the background.

124. CALIFORNIA GOLD MINERS: 1859

Miners Coming from Dinner, Granville Claim. Copy of an album print from a photograph attributed to Robert H. Vance. From the Vollum Collection of Gold Rush photographs.

The album of original prints is at the George Eastman House, Rochester, N. Y., from which the Library of Congress received photocopies. This is a typical miners' community, with wooden shacks, a dining hall, and a sluice in the valley.

125. MASSACHUSETTS STREET, LAWRENCE, KANSAS: 1867

From Alexander Gardner's stereograph, autumn of 1867.

Lawrence was founded in 1854 by the New England Emigrant Aid Co., and was named for Amos A. Lawrence of Boston, a prominent member of the company. It was the Free State capital of Kansas, and later became a market center and the site of the University of Kansas. LC–USZ62–7789

126. METROPOLIS OF EASTERN KANSAS: 1867

Fifth Street, Leavenworth. From Alexander Gardner's stereograph, autumn of 1867.

Leavenworth, a typical Missouri River trading town, for many years was an outfitting and financial center for the Western and Southwestern frontiers. This view includes Gardner's photographic wagon (right). LC–USZ62–11014

127. KANSAS PRAIRIE COW TOWN: 1867

South Side Main Street, Ellsworth. From Alexander Gardner's stereograph, autumn of 1867.

This view shows the unpainted wooden buildings, resembling a "Western" movie set. In the 1860's and 1870's Ellsworth was a boisterous cattle market, where "Buffalo Bill" Cody and "Wild Bill" Hickok were well-known guests of the Grand Central Hotel. LC–USZ62–7807

128. ALEXANDER GARDNER'S OUTFIT ON THE KANSAS FRONTIER: 1867

A Rare Specimen Found on Hill above Fort

KAYAKS AND NATIVES, PROVEN, GREENLAND; *Greely Expedition, 1881.* (See entry 120.)

THE GREAT FLOOD IN DENVER, COLO., 1864. *Cherry Creek on a rampage.* (See entry 130.)

34

Riley, Kans. From Gardner's stereograph, autumn 1867.

Gardner, a Scottish chemist, journalist, and photographer, came to America to join Mathew B. Brady, and became the manager of his gallery in Washington, D. C. Later Gardner established his own gallery there and became a great Civil War photographer. In 1867 he made a pictorial history of the frontier for the Union Pacific Railroad. LC–USZ62–11000

129. BLACK HAWK CITY, COLORADO TERRITORY: 1864

By George D. Wakely, a pioneer Rocky Mountain photographer.

This is one of a series of views of Colorado towns and scenic beauties, copyrighted by Wakely on October 14, 1864. The original gold-toned prints are mounted in the copyright record book of the First Judicial District, Colorado Territory, which was transferred to the Library of Congress about 1870. LC–USZ62–5346

130. DENVER'S CHERRY CREEK ON A RAMPAGE: 1864

By George D. Wakely.

This is one of six photographs which Wakely copyrighted on October 14, 1864, with the title "The Great Flood in Denver, Colorado Territory, May 19th, 1864." It is probably one of the earliest American photographs of a flood. The original print is mounted in the copyright record book of the First Judicial District, Colorado Territory. LC–USZ62–5349

131. PLACER MINING, TUOLUMNE COUNTY, CALIFORNIA: ca. 1866

From a photograph made for *Gems of California Scenery*, third edition, published in 1866 by George S. Lawrence and Thomas Houseworth, an optical equipment firm in San Francisco and New York.

The mounted photoprints in the Library of Congress contain a documentary record of life in California and Nevada. The firm employed several eminent photographers, including Carleton E. Watkins, whose large Yosemite photographs attracted keen attention at the Paris Exposition in 1867. LC–USZ62–5440

132. WASHING GOLD FROM THE HILLS: ca. 1866

From a photograph made for *Gems of California Scenery*, published by Lawrence and Houseworth, 1866.

This scene, probably in Tuolumne County, Calif., or in the vicinity, illustrates the picturesque method of hydraulic mining by powerful jets of water LC–USZ62–9889

133. LONG HAUL OVER THE MOUNTAINS: ca. 1866

Swift's Station, Carson and Lake Bigler Road. From a photograph made for *Gems of California Scenery*, published by Lawrence and Houseworth, 1866.

Swift's Station was at the eastern summit of the Sierra Nevada Mountains, on the road from California to Nevada. The photographer captured a scene illustrating transportation to California before the opening of the Union Pacific Railroad in 1869. LC–USZ62–11012

134. RIP-ROARING VIRGINIA CITY: ca. 1866

Wells, Fargo & Co.'s Express Office, C Street, Virginia City [Nev.]. From a photograph made for *Gems of California Scenery*, published by Lawrence and Houseworth, 1866.

Wells, Fargo & Co. played a major role in the development of the West. Virginia City was then the fabulously prosperous and exciting queen city of the Comstock Lode silver-mining operations. LC–USZ62–11055

VIGNETTES OF THE DAKOTA FRONTIER: ca. 1888–91

By J. C. H. Grabill of Deadwood, S. Dak., who established his studio when the Dakotas were still "Dakota Territory" and Deadwood was a boisterous trade center for the Black Hills mines. The following 5 photographs are from a collection depicting Indian and army life, cattle ranching, mining towns, stage-coaching, and frontier life.

135. THE U. S. PAYMASTER AND GUARDS ON DEADWOOD ROAD TO FORT MEADE: 1888 LC–USZ6–11

WELLS, FARGO & CO.'S EXPRESS OFFICE, VIRGINIA CITY, NEV., ca. 1866. (See entry 134.)

36

U. S. PAYMASTER AND GUARDS, DEADWOOD ROAD TO FORT MEADE, DAKOTA TERRITORY, 1888. (See entry 135.)

37

136. THE DEADWOOD COACH: 1889

This is the type of famous vehicle that figured in some actual Indian fights and holdups, and in many more staged ones in the ring of Buffalo Bill's Wild West show. LC–USZ62–5072

137. "WE HAVE IT RICH!": 1889

Three oldtime miners of the Black Hills—named Spriggs, Lamb, and Dillon—wash and pan gold at Rockerville, Dakota Territory.
LC–USZ62–7120

138. BRANDING CALVES ON ROUND UP: 1889 LC–USZ62–10932

139. OX TEAMS AT STURGIS, D. T. (Dakota Territory)

Sturgis is located in the Black Hills region of South Dakota, northeast of Deadwood.
LC–USZ62–11044

140. STUDIO OF LATON A. HUFFMAN, FRONTIER PHOTOGRAPHER: *ca.* 1878

Ye Studio—La Atelier, 18 x 40. Three rooms.
It was built of cottonwood logs with an earth roof, and Huffman occupied it upon his arrival at Fort Keogh, Mont., in December 1878. He was unofficial post photographer, guide to hunting parties, hunter for buffalo hides, and cattle rancher. Many years before his death at Miles City in 1931, he recorded in photographs the frontier of Montana, Wyoming, and the Dakotas.

141. "GENERAL SHERIDAN AND PARTY— OLD FAITHFUL IN ACTION": 1882

Huffman became noted for his views of scenic wonders in Yellowstone Park. On one occasion he encountered General Sheridan of Civil War fame, and photographed him (seated in the center) and his party, with "Old Faithful" geyser in the background. All Huffman photographs displayed in this exhibit have been used by permission of Mark H. Brown, and appear in his *The Frontier Years; L. A. Huffman, Photographer of the Plains* (New York, Henry Holt & Co., 1955).

142. "BUFFALO SKINNERS. TAKING THE MONSTER'S ROBE, NORTH MONTANA, JAN. 1882."

Huffman was one of the few photographers to take pictures of the buffalo on the open range, before the hunters and the skinners practically exterminated the animal. This picture shows the skinners working in bitterly cold weather and using the skinning wedge.

143. RECALLING THE CUSTER FIGHT

"Brave Wolf and Squaw Interviewed About Custer Fight. Squint Eye Interpreter. June 20, 1901."
Brave Wolf, a minor chief and medicine man of the Cheyennes, is seen here telling his story to an interpreter. The chief served as a scout for General Miles in the expedition of 1876 to pursue Sitting Bull, the Sioux leader, and was noted for his gracious manners and his "gift of prophecy."

144. LEADERS OF THE INDIAN'S LAST STAND: *ca.* 1879

"Dull Knife (right) and Bobtail Horse at Huffman's old log studio at Fort Keogh."
Dull Knife, a chief of the Northern Cheyennes, fought against General Crooks in the autumn of 1876. In 1878, the year of Huffman's arrival at Fort Keogh, he led in the escape of his people from a reservation in Indian Territory to Montana, and made a last stand in the Badlands hills.

145. "GUARD MOUNT IN BUFFALO COATS, FORT KEOGH": *ca.* 1880

Fort Keogh, a few miles from Milestown (now Miles City), for a time was Huffman's home and headquarters. The icicles hanging from the eaves of the veranda suggest the bitterly cold weather in which he took this picture.
This photograph reveals the fact that even at remote outposts of the United States Army, the band was there to bolster morale. One wonders how some of the men could keep their lips from sticking to the instruments in the bitter cold.

38

146. MILESTOWN, CAPITAL OF THE MONTANA PLAINS: 1881

This picture was taken on March 3, 1881, during a flood of the Tongue and Yellowstone Rivers: "Looking East on Main Street from Fifth. Charlie Brown's place left foreground (just beyond Breadwater, Hubbell & Co.) Cottage Saloon opposite." The buildings, mostly saloons and stores, give the impression of a typical "Western" movie set.

147. "ONLY AND ORIGINAL 'CALAMITY JANE' ": 1880

"Calamity Jane" was a character of the Dakota and Montana frontier between 1875 and 1895, well known in Miles City and Deadwood, and the subject of some hair-raising tales of dubious authenticity. She wore male attire (probably to help get jobs driving wagons), and served as a teamster in General Crooks' campaign of 1876 against the Sioux chief, Sitting Bull.

148. "MONTANA MAN-HUNTERS OF THE SEVENTIES BEFORE THE RAILROAD CAME"

These upholders of the law on the Great Plains were especially active in the 1870's. Left to right: Billy Smith (later a stock inspector); Jack Hawkins (formerly a Texas Ranger); Tom Irvine (Montana sheriff); Louis King (saloon-keeper); and "Eph" Davis (frontiersman). Irvine was a warm friend of the frontier photographer.

149. SHIPS OF THE GREAT PLAINS

"Covered Wagons on West Main Street, 1882."
This view in Miles City shows how the trains of white-covered wagons full of freight used to block the streets of frontier towns, while the air was thick with the oaths and whip-crackings of the bull-whackers who drove them. Typical are the unpaved street, the log construction and false fronts of some of the buildings, and the blacksmith and harness shops.

150. CONTRAST ON THE FRONTIER: ca. 1889

"Advance of Civilization, N. P. Express."

The opening of the Northern Pacific Railroad, through Montana to Puget Sound in 1889, marked the end of the frontier period, of the old freight wagons, and of the Indian tepee, seen here beside the train.

RANCHING IN EASTERN MONTANA: 1886

These photographs by Laton A. Huffman were reproduced by permission of Mark H. Brown, Alta, Iowa. They are illustrations in *Before Barbed Wire*, by Mark H. Brown and W. R. Felton.

151. "THE N BAR CROSSING, POWDER RIVER, 1886"

152. "THROWING RANGERS TO THE ROUNDUP"

153. "GOING TO THE ROUNDUP"

154. MONUMENT ON THE CUSTER BATTLEFIELD: 1876

From a stereograph by Stanley J. Morrow, Yankton, Dakota Territory; one of a series of "Photographic Views from the Great Northwest."

Not long after the battle of the Little Big Horn, in which the Sioux annihilated Gen. George A. Custer's force, Captain Sanderson, U. S. A., was ordered to gather the bones of the slain, and erect a monument to contain all remains found on the field.   LC–USZ62–9235

155. SANDERSON'S CAMP: 1876

From a stereograph by Stanley J. Morrow, Yankton, Dakota Territory.

The captain and his men occupied this camp at the ford on the Little Big Horn River in southeastern Montana, while they gathered the bones and erected a monument. Morrow was a Wisconsin veteran of the Civil War, and is said to have been trained by Mathew B. Brady. He settled at Yankton in 1870, and now is best known for his views of the Custer battlefield and of frontier forts.   LC–USZ62–11021

REFGEES FROM INDIAN MASSACRE IN MINNESOTA, 1862. *From a stereograph.* (See entry 156.)

156. FUGITIVES FROM INDIAN MASSACRE, MINNESOTA: 1862

By J. E. Whitney; one of his series, "Gems of Minnesota Scenery," issued by Whitney's Gallery in St. Paul and copyrighted in 1867 in the Federal District Court for Minnesota.

Resenting the failure of the United States Government to honor its promises to them, the Sioux rose under Chief Little Crow and massacred 800 settlers in the upper Minnesota River Valley. These refugees were photographed at dinner on a prairie. LC–USZ62–11024

157. SCENE FROM LIFE AMONG THE NAVAJOS: *ca.* 1871–74

Original print by Timothy H. O'Sullivan, for Geographical and Geological Explorations and Surveys West of the 100th Meridian, commanded by Lt. George M. Wheeler, Corps of Engineers.

After brilliantly assisting Mathew B. Brady in photographing the Civil War, O'Sullivan devoted himself to recording official surveys of the West. Wheeler glowingly praised O'Sullivan's work, and used it to make lithographs for his reports.

158. SUN DANCE AT PUEBLO DE COCHITI: 1888

By Charles F. Lummis, author and editor.

Sick from overwork as a newspaper editor in Los Angeles, in 1888 Lummis went to New Mexico to recuperate, and lived among the Pueblo Indians to learn their way of life. He devoted the rest of his career to making known the Spanish, Mexican, and Indian cultures of the Southwest, recorded Spanish and Indian songs, and founded and built the Southwest Museum in Los Angeles. LC–USZ62–8249

PUEBLO INDIANS PLAYING PATOL, NEW MEXICO, 1890. (See entry 159.)

159. PUEBLO INDIANS PLAYING PATOL: 1890

By Charles F. Lummis.

This is one of a series of photographs taken in 1888–94 in Isleta and vicinity, New Mexico, mostly illustrating the way of life of the Pueblo Indians. The series includes archeological sites, religious ceremonies, farming, games, dances, children, groups, and individual portraits.

LC–USZ62–8250

160. SANTA FÉ UNMODERNIZED: ca. 1885

San Francisco Street, by W. Henry Brown.

In the 1880's Brown made a series of stereoscopic views of the ancient capital of the Southwest, which then was still a typical Spanish *pueblo*. The series includes also the Governor's Palace, the plaza, churches, the oldest house, general views of the town, and scenes from Indian life in the vicinity.

LC–USZ62–11015

161. ON THE KLONDIKE GOLD TRAIL: 1897

Actresses on Way to Klondike Fording Dyea River, by Frank La Roche of Seattle, the chief point of departure in the Klondike gold rush.

The ladies were on their way to the mining-camp theaters and music halls. This series includes various aspects of the rush, Alaskan Indian life, and views of towns.

LC–USZ62–10912

162. HARDSHIPS OF THE TRAIL: 1897

Four Men Hitched to Cart, Fording Dyea River, by Frank La Roche of Seattle.

The struggles of would-be miners on the rugged

ACTRESSES ON THE WAY TO THE KLONDIKE MINES, 1897. (See entry 161.)

road to the Klondike are mildly suggested by the straining of these men.　　LC–USZ62–10929

163. SEEKING A FORTUNE, KLONDIKE REGION: 1897

Washing Out Gold, by Frank La Roche of Seattle.

This was the way all the adventurers hoped to "pan" a fortune—but few ever did.

　　　　　　　　　LC–USZ62–10928

164. KLONDIKE MINERS JUST LANDED: 1897

Klondike Outfits on the Rocks near Dyea, Alaska, by Winter and Pond, Juneau, Alaska.

Floyd V. Winter and Edwin P. Pond started a photographic firm in Juneau to produce views for commercial sale. Their work included a wide variety of scenes, some of which were reproduced in albums in 1909 and 1915 by the

Albertype Co. of Brooklyn, N. Y. (formerly Wittemann Bros.).　　　　LC–USZ62–10921

165. ON THE SUMMIT OF CHILKOOT PASS: 1897

By Winter and Pond, Juneau, Alaska.

Gold-seekers are resting at this high point on the toilsome and dangerous trail from the Alaskan coast to the far inland Klondike region on the Yukon River. Many perished on the journey.

　　　　　　　　　LC–USZ62–10904

166. INDIAN VILLAGE, HOWKAN, ALASKA: 1897

By Winter and Pond, Juneau, Alaska.

Along with Frank La Roche of Seattle, Winter and Pond were among the earliest photographers to record the picturesque Indian life of Alaska, with its elaborate wood carvings, totem poles, curious burial customs, and exotic dances and crafts.　　　　　　LC–USZ62–11025

GOLD-SEEKERS ON THE SUMMIT OF CHILKOOT PASS; *Yukon Trail, Alaska.* (See entry 165.)

43

167. AN ALASKAN INDIAN CHIEF'S HOUSE: 1897

Interior of Chief Klart-Reech's House, Chilkat, Alaska, by Winter and Pond, Juneau, Alaska. Shows weird and elaborate carvings.

LC–USZ62–10926

Scenery

168. REVEALING THE AWESOME GRAND CANYON: 1871

Black Cañon, Colorado River, looking above from Camp 7, by Timothy H. O'Sullivan. Original print.

This is one of a remarkable series taken during Lt. George M. Wheeler's Geographical and Geological Explorations and Surveys West of the 100th Meridian. The boat pulled up in the cove contains Sullivan's photographic equipment and miniature darkroom. He learned to work under hardships while assisting Mathew B. Brady druing the Civil War.

169. ROUGHING IT WITH WILLIAM HENRY JACKSON: 1871

Camp on Yellowstone Lake, Yellowstone Series' 1871, by William Henry Jackson. Original print.

Jackson, one of the pioneer photographers of the Great West, was a sensitive artist and a lover of outdoor life. This view was taken during the United States Geological Survey of the Territories, supervised by his friend, Ferdinand V. Hayden. Jackson's work on this trip influenced the establishment of the Yellowstone National Park.

170. OLD FAITHFUL GEYSER IN ERUPTION: 1892

By the Jackson Photo Co., Denver, Colo. Original print.

William Henry Jackson devoted most of his long life to photographing Western scenic marvels, and founded his own company to promote interest and sales. A veteran of the Civil War, he became interested during a tour of the Union Pacific route in 1869, and as official photographer for Ferdinand V. Hayden's Geological and Geographical Survey of the Territories.

171. MAMMOTH HOT SPRINGS, TOP OF PULPITS, YELLOWSTONE PARK: 1892

By the Jackson Photo Co., Denver, Colo. Original print.

William Henry Jackson began his long career as a scenic photographer in 1868, by touring around Omaha with his darkroom on a buckboard wagon. His later pictures were the first ever made in many areas now famous for their scenic beauties. Jackson Canyon in Wyoming and Jackson Butte in the Mesa Verde were named for him.

172. A FRONTIER PHOTOGRAPHER TURNS TO SCENERY: 1883

Laton A. Huffman, *Catalog 1883*. *Huffman's Latest Yellowstone National Park Views*. Exhibited by permission of Mark H. Brown, author of *The Frontier Years*.

Although his fame rests chiefly upon his record of frontier life, scenic views were a large part of Huffman's business. In the 1880's he made several trips to the park—750 miles of hard travel with supplies and photographic equipment on packhorses. The pictures he made on a trip in 1882 made a special hit with the public.

173. SAINT AUGUSTINE, FLORIDA, BEFORE THE BOOM: 1886

Charlotte Street, by George Barker, one of the leading American commercial photographers of the late 19th century. Original print.

The street is unkempt but picturesque, rutted by donkey carts and overhung by quaint Spanish balconies. Barker devoted his brilliant talent to satisfying the popular taste for the romantic, and specialized in scenery, historic buildings, and daily life. His work won several prizes for excellence.

44

INDIAN VILLAGE AND TOTEM POLES, HOWKAN, ALASKA. (See entry 166.)

45

174. "WAY DOWN UPON THE SUWANEE":
1886

Silver Springs, by George Barker. Original print.

Florida scenery was one of Barker's specialties, and this view of the steamboat landing at Silver Springs is one of his best. His views of tropical rivers and vegetation probably influenced promotion of interest in Florida as a winter playground.   LC–USZ62–11102

175. MOONLIGHT ON THE ST. JOHN'S
RIVER, FLORIDA: 1886

By George Barker.
The Library's large collection of Barker's Florida photographs is an excellent documentary record of the State before the great tourist boom. It includes not only romantic views, but also street scenes, hotels, Negro and Indian life, and interesting glimpses of villages that have become large cities, like St. Petersburg.
                            LC–USZ62–10925

176. CAVE OF THE WINDS, NIAGARA
FALLS: 1888

Original print by George Barker, whose home and headquarters were at the falls.

Barker became nationally famous for photographing the falls and the rapids from many unusual vantage points, including some dangerous ones. One can imagine the difficulty of taking this view of the falls from below, amid the rocks and the fragile-looking wooden walks, nearly hidden in clouds of spray.   LC–USZ62–11103

177. LUNA ISLAND [NIAGARA] IN
WINTER: 1888

Original print by George Barker.
Barker and other scenic photographers of the period strove to capture the public fancy by unusual and exotic effects, often obtained under extreme difficulty. One of his most popular views was this one of trees laden with new snow, resembling fantastic coral formations.

46

The Sea

178. TOUGH WORK ON AN OLDTIME
WHALER: *ca.* 1900

Cutting in a Sperm Whale. Jaw Nearly Clear . . . , by H. S. Hutchinson & Co., New Bedford, Mass.

This and the following view have been selected from a series of about 20 remarkable photographs of whaling operations aboard the bark *California* off the coast of Japan. They are probably among the few ever taken of this industry, and show processes that had changed little since the days of Herman Melville. The crewmen are "cutting in" the whale, held by large hoisting chains and blocks.   LC–USZ62–7241

179. TRYING-OUT

Mincing the "Blubber," by H. S. Hutchinson & Co., New Bedford, Mass.

In his experience aboard a whaler, Herman Melville many times witnessed this hot, greasy, and dirty task. The men are slicing whale blubber into small pieces for melting down in huge vats set upon a brick furnace. Melville vividly describes trying-out in *Moby Dick*.
                            LC–USZ62–11042

180. ON SEAGIRT NANTUCKET: 1897

The Heart of 'Sconset, by Henry S. Wyer.
Wyer was a local photographer who in the period 1895–1914 published four books about the famous island off the Massachusetts coast. This view shows the sandy main thoroughfare of "'Sconset" (Siasconset) with its quaint houses.
                            LC–USZ62–11029

181. A NANTUCKET VISTA: 1897

By Henry S. Wyer.
The horse and buggy and the ancient windmill suggest the quiet character of the island before its modernization and the arrival of the automobile. In the 18th and early 19th centuries Nantucket was inhabited largely by Quakers, and was a renowned center of the whale fishery. There were Nantucketers on the whaler that carried Herman Melville to the Pacific Ocean.
                            LC–USZ62–11045

MOONLIGHT ON THE ST. JOHN'S RIVER, FLORIDA, 1886. (See entry 175.)

47

182. TOTE THAT BALE!: *ca.* 1900

Unloading Cotton at Levee, Memphis, Tenn. From a Detroit Publishing Co. collection, this illustrates the methods of loading and unloading ships at Southern and Great Lakes ports around the turn of the century. Others in the series include such cargoes as copper in Michigan and fruit at New Orleans. LC–D4–19391

LIFE IN THE UNITED STATES NAVY: 1890–1900

These 3 photographs are from a collection of about 2,500, formerly owned by the Detroit Publishing Co. Many of them were taken by E. H. Hart of Brooklyn, N. Y., and were acquired by the company, in which William H. Jackson, the well-known Western photographer, was a partner.

MINCING BLUBBER ON THE WHALER, "CALIFORNIA," *ca.* 1900. (See entry 179.)

183. BERTH DECK COOKS, U. S. S. "MAINE"

This ship was sunk by a mine in Havana Harbor, Cuba, February 15, 1898.
LC–D4–21074

184. TAILORING ABOARD THE U. S. S. "NEW HAMPSHIRE"   LC–D4–20705

185. CHIEF PETTY OFFICERS OF THE U. S. S. "NEWARK"   LC–D4–20068

Occupations

186. GLIMPSE OF THE RISING OIL INDUSTRY

Oil City Refinery, by Wittemann Bros., showing the largest crude-oil stills.

Wittemann Bros. started their immense post-card and souvenir booklet business shortly after the Civil War, and traveled extensively, taking photographs of notable views, including many "local color" pictures.   LC–W6–274

187. OIL TOWN, WESTERN PENNSYLVANIA

Probably Oil City. This was taken by Witte-mann Bros., whose views were printed mainly by the photogelatin process directly from the glass plates. The firm later became the Albertype Co. of Brooklyn, N. Y., one of the world's largest publishers of photographic cards and booklets. Few aspects of American life escaped their lens.
LC–W6–267

188. LUMBERING

Largest Load [of Logs] Ever Hauled: 1895. By W. G. Hopps, Rush City, Minn.

The load was hauled on Washington's birthday, at the Rutledge Lumber Co.'s camp, 15 miles from Rutledge. It consisted of 56 long logs, containing over 37,000 feet of lumber and making

a pile 26 feet high. The picture illustrates the old method of getting out lumber in winter on huge sleds.   LC–USZ62–10927

189. SECRET PHOTOGRAPH, NEW YORK STOCK EXCHANGE: ca. 1907

By the Pearson Publishing Co.

Taking pictures was strictly forbidden, and this one was snapped with a camera concealed in the photographer's sleeve to evade the vigilant stock exchange guards. The feat was performed for *Pearson's Magazine* to illustrate an article on the exchange.   LC–USZ62–11035

190. ORGAN–GRINDER AND HIS WIFE, NEW YORK: 1897

By Mrs. E. A. Austen.

The photographer made a collection of photographs illustrating street types of the great city. They are interesting as early documentary records of American urban life, and perhaps were inspired by the example of Jacob Riis, who explored the slums with the camera and wrote a sensational book about them, *How the Other Half Lives.*   LC–USZ62–11036

191. THE FEATHER-DUSTER MAN, CHICAGO: 1891

By Sigmund Krausz.

This is one of a collection of photographs taken by Krausz for his study of street types. He used them to illustrate his two books: *Street Types of Chicago . . . with Literary Sketches by Well-Known Local Authors* (Chicago, 1892), and *Street Types of Great American Cities* (Chicago and New York, 1896).   LC–USZ62–5433

192. THE BILL-POSTER, CHICAGO: 1891

Another of Sigmund Krausz's studies of street types. Others show a street fakir, beerman, accordion-player, iceman, organ-grinder, berryman, scissors-grinder, newsboy, and match boy. The portraits are "posed," but are of high technical quality and reveal a genuine understanding of character. They have been described as "exceptional Americana."   LC–USZ62–11022

UNLOADING COTTON AT THE LEVEE, MEMPHIS, TENN., ca. 1900. (See entry 182.)

THE ORGAN-GRINDER AND HIS WIFE, NEW YORK CITY, 1897. (See entry 190.)

Urban Life and Work

CITY SCENES AROUND THE TURN OF
THE CENTURY

193. WEST WASHINGTON MARKET, NEW YORK

By Wittemann Bros.

A scene lively with wagons of produce, stalls, and buyers. This and the following 7 views are from glass plate negatives made by Wittemann Bros., who for two generations after the Civil War took innumerable documentary and scenic photographs for their enormous postcard and album business. The brothers traveled all over the United States, and specialized in "local color." LC–W6–222

194. BROOKLYN BRIDGE

The towers rise over the tenements, business buildings, ferry houses, street markets, and shops of lower Manhattan. LC–W6–231

195. PANORAMA OF NEW YORK HARBOR

The sweeping view was taken from the Brooklyn waterfront and includes the southern end of Manhattan Island, Jersey City in the distance, three-masted sailing vessels at the piers, and ferries crossing. LC–W6–229

51

PANORAMA OF NEW YORK HARBOR, *before 1900.* (See entry 195.)

52

MARDI GRAS PROCESSION, NEW ORLEANS, *before 1900*. (See entry 197.)

EAST SIDE PUBLIC SCHOOL, NEW YORK CITY, *early 1890's.* (See entry 204.)

URBAN LIFE

196. SCISSORS-GRINDER, NEW ORLEANS

He carries a grinding machine on his shoulders and a toolbox hanging from his neck.

LC–W6–158

197. MARDI GRAS PROCESSION, NEW ORLEANS

The view includes such typical features of the Crescent City as the ornamental iron balcony and the horse-drawn streetcar.   LC–W6–153

198. FISHING FLEET AT THE LEVEE, NEW ORLEANS

This was one of the picturesque sights of the city half a century and more ago.   LC–W6–170

199. STREET VENDOR, NEW ORLEANS

She stands in front of a typical iron fence and carries a basket of market produce on her head in the Creole manner.   LC–W6–315

200. OUTDOOR MARKET, NEW ORLEANS

Taken some time in the 1890's.   LC–W6–328

201. FRUIT SELLER, NEW ORLEANS

By Frances Benjamin Johnston.

Miss Johnston, one of our earliest documentary photographers, rivaled the Wittemann Bros. in gathering "local color." Born in West Virginia, she studied art in Paris, and became a newspaper correspondent and interviewer in Washington, D. C., where she had her chief studio. For more than half a century after 1888 she was a noted

54

news and feature photographer, with a special interest in the South. LC–J713–1419

202. WASHINGTON STUDIO OF FRANCES BENJAMIN JOHNSTON: 1890's

The studio was located on V Street NW., between 13th and 14th Streets. At the time this picture was taken, Miss Johnston was well-launched upon her noted career as a feature and documentary photographer. Interesting features of the picture are the rolling camera stand and the screen to regulate light. LC–J713–1

203. MISS JOHNSTON OFF FOR A PHOTO-GRAPHIC TOUR: 1895

A copy of her advertisement, designed by Mills Thompson. Frances Benjamin Johnston was one of the earliest photographers to make a special business of gathering photographic illustrations for articles in periodicals. LC–J713–8769

LIFE AMONG THE NEW YORK POOR: EARLY 1890's

204. EAST SIDE PUBLIC SCHOOL

By Jacob August Riis, journalist, author, and social reformer.

Riis came to the United States from Denmark in 1869 at the age of 20, became a reporter for the New York *Sun*, and by his lectures and writings aroused interest in improving the lot of the downtrodden. This and the two following scenes are typical of many used to illustrate his books, *How the Other Half Lives* (1890) and *Battle with the Slums* (1902) LC–USZ62–11023

205. SHOOTING CRAPS IN THE HALL OF THE NEWSBOYS' LODGING HOUSE
LC–USZ62–11032

206. A VEGETABLE STAND IN THE MULBERRY STREET BEND

"With myself (Riis) in the picture."
LC–USZ62–11034

Down on the Farm

COUNTRY LIFE ON THE WINCHESTER ROAD, VIRGINIA: 1890's

207. OLD TURNPIKE TOLL GATE

With keeper's house, toll booth, and barrier, by Frances Benjamin Johnston.

This and the seven following views date from the earliest phase of Miss Johnston's career, when she was traveling about the country to make "local color" and documentary photographs. The series depicts aspects of rural life over 60 years ago, about 70 or 80 miles west of Washington. LC–J713–1133

208. CHANGING HORSES

Putting a horse into the shafts of a covered wagon, near an old-fashioned picket fence.
LC–J682–2

209. FERRY

The antique rustic kind, poled across the stream by one-manpower. LC–J682–1

210. ROAD-BUILDING

A human stonebreaker and a typical two-horse wagon. LC–J713–1140

211. OX TEAM

A typical scene from rural Negro life. The log cabin with slab roof and stone chimney is a survival from a still earlier day. LC–J713–1148

212. DRAWING WATER

The old-fashioned enclosed well has a long "sweep." LC–J713–1150

213. HOG-KILLING

The animals are suspended from a pole supported by crotched sticks, before a log cabin with a shingled roof. LC–J713–1149

RUSTIC FERRY IN VIRGINIA, 1890's. (See entry 209.)

TINTYPE BOOTH AT A COUNTY FAIR IN VIRGINIA. (See entry 214.)

FIRST PASSENGER TRAIN OVER THE OHIO RIVER BRIDGE, LOUISVILLE, KY., 1870. (See entry 217.)

214. TINTYPE BOOTH AT THE COUNTY FAIR: MAY 1903

Frances Benjamin Johnston is seated at the table before her decorated tent booth, on the green in front of the county courthouse, and nearby stands a "barker" with his horn.

LC–J713–4931

215. SOD HOUSE FARM FAMILY, NEBRASKA: 1887

By Solomon Devore Butcher.

Butcher made an extensive series of photographs of pioneer settlers and their homes for his *Pioneer History of Custer County and Short Sketches of Early Days in Nebraska* (Broken Bow, 1901). Several thousands of his original negatives are in the collections of the State Historical Society, Lincoln, Nebr. The sod house was the natural shelter for early settlers on the treeless plains, and examples still exist. LC–USZ62–7783

Transportation

216. EXHIBIT OF THE HORSE-DRAWN ERA: *ca.* 1900

Omaha Merchants Express & Transfer Co., by F. J. Bandholtz, Des Moines, Iowa. Original print.

Bandholtz traveled about Iowa, Kansas, and Nebraska, making panoramic views of the main street intersections of many small towns. This

58

picture includes vehicles of which Americans now know little or nothing; but they can easily recognize "the surrey with the fringe on top," in the middle.

217. NEW RAILROAD BRIDGE, LOUISVILLE, KY.: 1870

The First Passenger Train Passing Over the Great Ohio River Bridge at Louisville, Ky. February 18, 1870, by E. Klauber, Louisville.

LC–USZ62–10913

218. CELEBRATING THE RAILROAD'S WESTWARD MARCH: 1866

The Directors of the U. P. R. R. at the 100th Mer[idian]. From a stereograph by John Carbutt, Chicago.

When the rails reached the meridian, about 250 miles west of Omaha, the directors organized a special excursion to interest Eastern capitalists. The gala party of distinguished persons and reporters had chefs and two brass bands. Carbutt joined as an official photographer. LC–USZ62–5447

219. THE CAMERA FOLLOWS THE RAILROAD: *ca.* 1868–9

Engine No. 5 and Photograph Car taken near Point of Rocks, Wyoming. From the files of the Association of American Railroads.

The photograph car closely followed the mile-a-day advance of the rails, while the camera recorded life in the uproarious construction camps. LC–USZ62–11037

220. LARGEST STEAMBOAT EVER BUILT IN THE WEST: 1870

Cabin of Steamer "James Howard." One of a collection of photographs of Mississippi and Ohio River steamboats, 1860–90's, mainly from the Howard Shipyard, Jeffersonville, Ind., presented to the Library of Congress by the collector, Garrett Laidlaw Eskew of Chicago.

The "James Howard," designed by Thomas Bell, was 330 feet long, 54 feet beam, 10 feet hold, and had 6 boilers. LC–USZ63–6
LC–USZ62–11010

221. PILOT HOUSE OF A BIG RIVER BOAT

Pilot House of the J. M. White III, by J. Mack Moore. From an extensive collection concerning river steamboats, 1860–90's, presented to the Library of Congress by the collector, Garrett Laidlaw Eskew of Chicago.

In a pilot house like this Mark Twain learned the quirks of the Mississippi. LC–USZ62–4809

222. OHIO RIVER STERN-WHEELER: *ca.* 1890

Ohio River Steam Boat, at Blennerhassett Island, by Frances Benjamin Johnston.

LC–J713–2

223. AN EARLY FREAK AIRCRAFT

By Wittemann Bros., undated, but probably about 1900.

Little of interest escaped the lens of the Wittemanns, who scoured the country for unusual sights to attract the innumerable buyers of their postcards and albums. This probably is one of the earliest photographs of an aerial machine.

LC–W6–390

224. AERIAL RECONNAISSANCE IN THE CIVIL WAR

Prof. Lowe Inflating His Balloon on Gaine's Hill, Va. By Mathew B. Brady or one of his assistants.

The site probably was near Gainesville, west of Manassas. Thaddeus S. C. Lowe (1832–1913) in the late 1850's constructed balloons to study atmospheric conditions, and during the Civil War he headed an aeronautical corps in the Union Army. The balloons were ineffective, because they were not easily controlled and were conspicuous targets. LC–BH816–2350

225. GETTING READY TO TAKE AERIAL VIEWS: *ca.* 1886

[Balloon Flight over Connecticut] by John J. Doughty and Alfred E. Moore.

On the voyage they took views of Riverton, Simsbury, Windsor, and Winsted. In this picture they and two assistants are preparing the balloon bag for the flight. LC–USZ62–11027

CABIN OF THE RIVER STEAMBOAT, "JAMES HOWARD," JEFFERSONVILLE, IND. (See entry 220.)

FUNERAL OF EX-PRESIDENT ANDREW JOHNSON, GREENEVILLE, TENN., 1875. *From a stereograph.* (See entry 226.)

Presidents

226. WHERE ANDREW JOHNSON LAY IN STATE: 1875

The Court House at Greeneville, Tenn., August 3, 1875. From a stereograph by L. W. Keen of Jonesboro, Tenn.

The flag suspended in the middle of the street was captured from General Rosecrans at the Battle of Chickamauga, and was recaptured in North Carolina by General Stoneman. At the time of his death, ex-President Johnson was serving as United States Senator from Tennessee. His home and his tailor shop still stand in Greeneville.   LC–USZ62–10998

227. "UNCONDITIONAL SURRENDER" GRANT

Printed by Ansco, Binghamton, N. Y., from a glass plate by Mathew B. Brady.

This and the two following portraits are from plates discovered in his barn at Owego, N. Y., by George L. Andrews, former district attorney of Tioga County, N. Y. Andrews sold the plates to Ansco, the Nation's oldest photographic manu-

GENERAL ULYSSES S. GRANT AND FAMILY, MOUNT MCGREGOR, N. Y., 1886.   (See entry 230.)

facturer, whose predecessors, Edward Anthony & Co. and E. and H. T. Anthony & Co., supplied Brady with most of his materials.

228. JOHN ALEXANDER LOGAN AND FAMILY

Portrait printed by Ansco, Binghamton, N. Y., from a glass plate made by Mathew B. Brady.

Logan was United States Senator from Illinois and a strong supporter of President Ulysses S. Grant.

229. MADAME CATACAZY

Wife of the Russian Ambassador to the United States.   Portrait printed by Ansco, Binghamton, N. Y., from a glass plate made by Mathew B. Brady.

230. GRANT SHORTLY BEFORE HIS DEATH: 1886

General U. S. Grant and Family, At Mount McGregor, by the U. S. Instantaneous Photo Co.

When this picture was taken, Grant was stricken with cancer of the throat, and was fighting to live long enough to complete his *Personal Memoirs*. The famous book was written in his sickroom at Mount McGregor, and was published by Mark Twain.   LC–USZ62–10909

231. PRESIDENT GARFIELD AT HOME IN OHIO: *ca.* 1881

The Garfield and Rudolph Families, at the Rudolph Home in Hiram, O. From a stereograph by Stern & Gates, Garrettsville, Ohio.

James A. Garfield (1831–81) was a pupil, and

THE GARFIELD AND RUDOLPH FAMILIES, HIRAM, O., ca. 1881. *From a stereograph.* (See entry 231.)

served as teacher and principal, of the Institute (now Hiram College) in Hiram. In 1858 he married Lucretia Rudolph, his childhood playmate and a fellow student at the Institute.

LC–USZ62–10910

232. INTIMATE GLIMPSES OF McKINLEY: *ca.* 1900–01

President McKinley Speaking near the Scene of the Alamo Massacre, San Antonio, Texas. From a stereograph by Underwood and Underwood, 1901.

This and the two following photographs show the President on a speaking tour, and suggest the source of his great personal popularity—his unfailing geniality. LC–USZ62–11047

233. A MINER'S LITTLE DAUGHTER PHOTOGRAPHING THE PRESIDENT

In Arizona. From a stereograph by Underwood & Underwood, 1901.

LC–USZ62–10997

234. GREETING THE CHILDREN OF HIS OLD NEIGHBORS—PRESIDENT McKINLEY AT THE STATION, CANTON, OHIO

From a stereograph by Strohmeyer and Weyman, 1900. LC–USZ62–11007

235. PRESIDENT McKINLEY IN HIS OFFICE: 1898

From a glass plate negative by Frances Benjamin Johnston, probably taken during the Spanish-American War.

This portrait reveals the President's great dignity and handsome presence. The desk doubtless was the one from which McKinley used to take red carnations to present to men who came with angry complaints but went away pacified. LC–J713–1507

236. IDA SAXTON McKINLEY: 1897

From a glass plate negative by Frances Benjamin Johnston.

63

A beautiful portrait, giving an impression of delicacy and refinement. Mrs. McKinley was the daughter of a banker in Canton, Ohio, where McKinley was practicing law when he married her in 1871. Her family were among the founders of Canton. The McKinleys were a deeply devoted couple, and their relationship was made the more tender by the President's chivalrous care for her after she became an invalid.   LC–J713–8559

The Nation's Capital:
After the War

237. THE NAVY DEPARTMENT BUILDING: *ca.* 1867–69

From a stereoscopic view by Bell & Bro., Washington, D. C.

The Bell studio was at 319 Pennsylvania Avenue NW. This view shows one of the old horsecars that used to trundle across town from Capitol Hill to Washington Circle.

LC–USZ62–11048

238. EGG-ROLLING AT THE WHITE HOUSE, EASTER MONDAY: 1889

From a glass plate negative by Frances Benjamin Johnston, showing the crowd on the south lawn around the fountain.

Until 1887 the event took place in the Capitol Grounds, and after it was moved to the White House the President used to come out and shake hands with the people. This photograph is from the earliest phase of Miss Johnston's work, 1888–95, when she was making views of Washington institutions and residences. LC–J682–5

239. PLAYTIME AT THE WHITE HOUSE: *ca.* 1889

From a glass plate negative by Frances Benjamin Johnston, showing Maj. Russell Harrison and the Harrison children, with "Baby McKee" and his sister in a goat cart, early in the term of President Benjamin Harrison.   LC–J698–81266

240. THE WHITE HOUSE KITCHEN: *ca.* 1890

By Charles M. Bell of Bell & Bro., one of Washington's well-known photographers, who made a number of views of the White House.

LC–USZ62–4502

Spanish-American War:
1898

241. THE MAST OF THE "MAINE": FEB. 15, 1900

From a collection of Spanish-American War photographs presented to the Library of Congress in 1951 by the heirs of Gen. Hugh L. Scott, a noted Indian fighter.

The blowing-up of the "Maine" in Havana Harbor by a mine on February 15, 1898, made war between the United States and Spain inevitable. The mast now stands in the Arlington National Cemetery.   LC–USZ62–11020

242. THE ARMY LANDS IN CUBA: 1898

Landing of Am[erican] troops at Daiquiri, Cuba, by William Dinwiddie.

The object of the landing was to drive the Spanish forces out of Santiago by capturing the heights behind the city, especially the key position of San Juan Hill.   LC–USZ62–8724

243. THE ARMY MOVES AGAINST SANTIAGO, CUBA: 1898

Sixteenth Infantry in San Juan Creek bottom, under Spanish fire from San Juan Hill, July 1, by William Dinwiddie.

One of a large series of photographs. The campaign began when an American Army of 18,000 regular soldiers and volunteers was shipped in June from Tampa, Fla., to the coast of Cuba east of Santiago, under the command of Gen. W. R. Shafter.   LC–USZ62–534

244. "TEDDY" ROOSEVELT AND HIS ROUGH RIDERS: 1898

Rough Riders at the Top of the Hill which they Captured, Battle of San Juan, by William Dinwiddie.

Theodore Roosevelt, who raised and commanded the famous group, is seen in the center. The Rough Riders were part of the force that stormed and captured the heights overlooking Santiago in the Battles of El Caney and San Juan Hill, thus compelling the Spaniards to abandon the city.   LC–USZ62–7626

245. THE EASY CONQUEST OF PUERTO RICO: 1898

Custom's House. Wisconsin troops going to the front. From the Sherman Miles collection of photographs relating to the Spanish-American War, presented to the Library of Congress by General Miles, 1925.

An army commanded by Gen. Nelson A. Miles landed on the island on July 25 and occupied it almost without opposition.   LC–USZ62–11028

THE NAVY IN ACTION

From the files of the Detroit Photographic Co.

246. U. S. S. NEW YORK BOMBARDING AGUAPORES   LC–D4–20726

247. BURIAL AT SEA OF SEAMAN KILLED AT SAN JUAN   LC–D4–20788

248. U. S. S. IOWA. WATCHING BOMBARDMENT OF SAN JUAN DE PUERTO RICO   LC–D4–21072

THE MAST OF THE "MAINE," HAVANA HARBOR, 1900. (See entry 241.)

"TEDDY" ROOSEVELT AND HIS ROUGH RIDERS, SAN JUAN HILL, CUBA, 1898. (See entry 244.)

ADMIRAL GEORGE DEWEY'S TRIUMPH IN WASHINGTON, 1899. *With President McKinley and Cardinal Gibbons.*
(See entry 249.)

A FREAK OF THE JOHNSTOWN FLOOD, 1889. *From a stereograph.* (See entry 255.)

249. ADMIRAL GEORGE DEWEY'S TRIUMPH IN WASHINGTON: 1899

Pres^t McKinley and Admiral Dewey. The Benediction by Cardinal Gibbons, by William H. Rau.

After his defeat of the Spanish Fleet in the Battle of Manila Bay, May 1, 1898, Dewey remained in the Far East for about a year. He then returned to an ovation of unprecedented brilliance in New York and elsewhere. Congress voted him the title "Admiral of the Navy," and the Nation gave him a house in Washington. LC–USZ62–10908

250. OVATION TO ADMIRAL DEWEY IN NEW YORK: 1899

Sampson and Miles and Visitors leaving Admiral Dewey aboard the "Olympia," by William H. Rau.

The "Olympia" was Dewey's flagship at the Battle of Manila Bay. This is one of a series illustrating the brilliant spectacles that attended the welcome, including views of naval vessels in the Hudson, scenes aboard ship, and Dewey receiving distinguished visitors. LC–USZ62–11040

News Photography

251. THE METROPOLITAN FAIR, NEW YORK: 1864

Ice Cream Stand. One of 15 photographs of the fair, donated to the Library of Congress by Mrs. J. West Roosevelt.

The huge fair was held during the Civil War to raise money for ministering to soldiers in the field, in camps and hospitals, and on leave.
LC–USZ62–11008

252. WHAT THE FIRE LEFT OF CHICAGO: 1871

The Great Conflagration of Chicago. Original print, panoramic photograph in four sections by Shaw, special artist for Frank Leslie's Illustrated News.

The fire broke out on the night of October 8, and in a little over 24 hours razed most of the city, killing about 300 persons and making 100,000 persons homeless.

253. THE GREAT OHIO RIVER FLOOD: 1884

View of Lawrenceburg, Ind., by Rombach and Groene, Cincinnati, Ohio, showing the central part of the town in deep water, with the Ohio spreading in the distance. The Ohio River flood of 1884 was the greatest until that of 1936. The Red Cross carried on one of its earliest relief campaigns, led by Clara Barton. LC–USZ62–10931

254. APPALLING WRECKAGE OF THE JOHNSTOWN FLOOD: 1889

General View of Johnstown Looking Towards Kernville, by Histed, Pittsburgh, Pa.

The loss of life was estimated at 5,000 and the property damage at over $10,000,000. One of the most memorable aspects of the tragedy was the vast relief work, in which the Red Cross led by Clara Barton played a prominent part.
LC–USZ62–10916

255. A FREAK OF THE JOHNSTOWN FLOOD: 1889

A Slightly Damaged House. From a stereograph by George Barker of Niagara Falls.

The catastrophe to this western Pennsylvania town, on May 31, 1889, was caused by the collapse of a dam at the Conemaugh Reservoir during torrential rains. The deluge wiped out most of Johnstown and its suburbs, situated in a narrow valley. LC–USZ62–11049

256. AFTERMATH OF THE LOUISVILLE CYCLONE: 1890

Church of [the] Sacred Heart, by E. Klauber, Louisville.

The cyclone roared through the city on the evening of March 7, 1890, cutting a swath of utter devastation, killing over 100 persons, and wrecking some of the largest and strongest buildings, including even the Union Railway Station.
LC–USZ62–11041

"GENERAL" COXEY'S ARMY APPROACHING WASHINGTON, 1894. (See entry 258.)

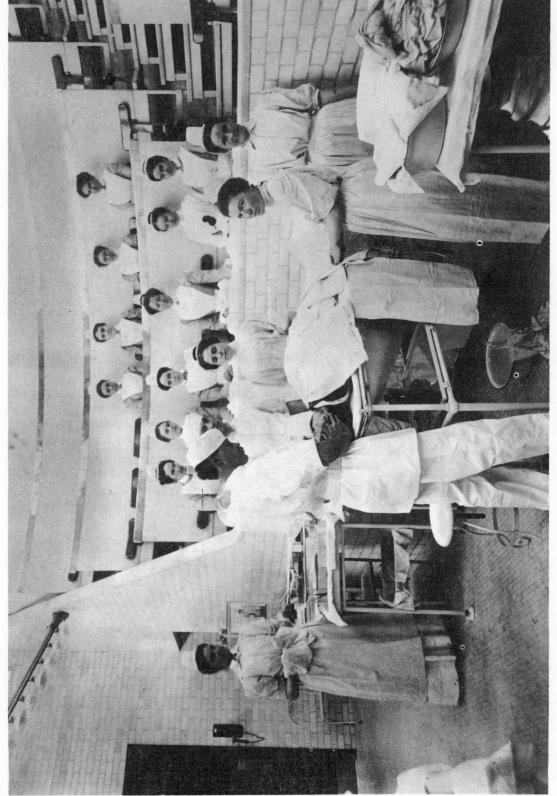

MAKING READY FOR AN OPERATION, ST. LUKE'S HOSPITAL, NEW YORK CITY. (See entry 259.)

71

257. INCIDENT OF THE HOMESTEAD STEEL STRIKE: 1892

The Station. Strikers Watching for "Scabs." Published by J. F. Jarvis, Washington, D. C., sold by Underwood & Underwood.

The strike was one of the contemporary news sensations, and is regarded as a landmark in the growth of American labor organization, even though the strikers lost their battle with the Carnegie Co. for recognition of their union.

LC–USZ62–11052

258. "GENERAL" COXEY'S ARMY APPROACHES WASHINGTON: 1894

From a photograph by Ray Stannard Baker.

Part of the "army" is shown on a barge at a lock in the Chesapeake & Ohio Canal. The march on Washington during the depression of 1894 was led by Jacob S. Coxey of Massillon, Ohio, a reformer who advocated large public works to relieve unemployment. About 500 men reached Washington, where Coxey was arrested when he tried to speak from the Capitol steps.

LC–USZ62–10919

259. PHOTOGRAPHY IN THE HOSPITAL: 1899

Making Ready for an Operation, St. Luke's Hospital, New York City, by R. F. Turnbull, New York.

This evidently was a demonstration for the benefit of nurses. LC–USZ62–10999

260. SCIENCE IN THE DENTIST'S OFFICE: ca. 1900

Hypnotism in Dentistry. Copyrighted in 1900 by the American College of Sciences.

LC–USŹ62–10915

261. MUYBRIDGE EXPERIMENTS IN PHOTOGRAPHING MOTION: 1877

Sallie Gardner, by Eadweard Muybridge (i. e., James Edward Muggeridge) at Palo Alto race track, California.

In the 1870's this English-born photographer devoted his attention to perfecting techniques for taking photographs of animals and people in motion. His views of running horses, sponsored by Leland Stanford, were made with a battery of cameras in a row, activated by the horses' breaking strings stretched across the track. In 1880 he projected moving pictures from his instantaneous photographs to the public.

LC–USZ62–5468

262. WORLD'S COLUMBIAN EXPOSITION, CHICAGO: 1893

Part of the Midway, by Frances Benjamin Johnston.

The exposition introduced the "Midway Plaisance" and the Ferris wheel, which have been stock features of great American fairs ever since. Extravagantly staged to celebrate the 400th anniversary of the landing of Columbus, the exposition really was a glorification of American progress and achievement, and introduced the classical "American Renaissance" in architecture.

LC–USZ62–10917

263. WORLD'S COLUMBIAN EXPOSITION, CHICAGO: 1893

Administration and Electrical Buildings, by Wittemann Bros. (later the Albertype Co.), Brooklyn, N. Y.

The exposition was a bonanza for this and other firms that specialized in photographic post cards and souvenir albums. Their pictures of the magnificent white exposition buildings, and of the wondering crowds, gave Americans a new sense of accomplishment. LC–USZ62–10918

Sports and Recreation

264. JOHN L. SULLIVAN KNOCKS OUT JAKE KILRAIN: 1889

Last Round—Victor and Vanquished, by George Barker, a leading commercial photographer.

This is said to have been the last great bare-knuckle championship bout in the United States; it was fought at Richburg, Miss., on July 8, 1889, under a blazing sun, and lasted for "seventy-five red rounds." LC–USZ62–10907

HIGH-WHEEL BICYCLE RIDERS, BOSTON, *before 1900*. *From a stereograph.* (See entry 271.)

265. "THE STRONG BOY OF BOSTON": 1889

John L. Sullivan, Sporting Editor. Original print, by J. Wood, Bowery, New York.

The champion appears in an unfamiliar pose, in the year of his famous victory over Jake Kilrain. Sullivan became a boxer at 19, and for 10 years after defeating Paddy Ryan in 1882 he dominated the prize ring. He was a spectacular personality in the world of sports, the owner of a diamond-studded belt given by Boston admirers.

266. "GENTLEMAN JIM" CORBETT: 1890

James J. Corbett. Original print by Richard K. Fox, Franklin Square, N. Y.

The handsome and speedy young boxer from San Francisco polished off Joe Choynski in 1889 and Jake Kilrain in 1890; 2 years later he knocked out John L. Sullivan in round 21. Corbett acquired his nickname from his pleasant demeanor and his popularity among rich sportsmen. After his ring days, he enjoyed a long career on the stage, in movies, and on radio.

267. HUNTING IN THE NORTHWEST: *ca.* 1890

Deer Hunters at Home. Deer and Pony, by T. W. Ingersoll. From a collection donated to the Library of Congress by Mrs. Gladys G. Wittemann (of Wittemann Bros.).

The pictures illustrate various aspects of hunting, such as log cabin camp houses, portaging, lying in wait for ducks, shooting from horseback, eating lunch *al fresco*, and posing with the day's trophies. LC–USZ62–10914

268. GOOD SHOOTING IN THE ADIRONDACKS: 1889

In the Adirondacks. [Hunters returning with a Deer.] Original print by Seneca Roy Stoddard, Glens Falls, N. Y., a noted scenic photographer, who compiled numerous picture albums featuring vacation life and mountain scenery.

269. "PHIL" SHERIDAN ENTERTAINS A GRAND DUKE: 1872

The Imperial Hunting Party, by J. Lee Knight, Topeka, Kans.

The Civil War general was host to the Grand Duke Alexis of Russia and his suite, on a hunting expedition to the Far West. The visit was one of the sensational events of the time.

LC–USZ62–11033

270. ENGLISH ATMOSPHERE IN SPORT: *ca.* 1900

Chevy Chase Hunt. Original print by the Burr McIntosh Studio, New York.

The hunt evidently is ready to start early in the morning, like the English fox-hunts.

271. THE HIGH-WHEELERS OF THE 1880'S

Our Jay-Eye-See, The Bicycle. From a stereograph by an unidentified photographer.

The scene is on the plaza near Trinity Church in Boston. LC–USZ62–11019

272. WHAT THE LADY CYCLIST WILL WEAR: 1895

Mrs. L. C. Boardman. Original print by George H. Van Norman, Springfield, Mass.

For the truly fashionable the buttoned leggings, tailored suit, and derby hat were indispensable.

273. GIBSON GIRLS READY FOR THE COURTS: 1895

All United States International Tennis Players. Original print by Gilbert & Bacon, Philadelphia.

Nobody today could imagine young American women playing any game in such costumes, but these 14 held their own in the full rig so often depicted by Charles Dana Gibson on magazine covers.

274. BIG-LEAGUE BASEBALL TEAM: 1886

Opening of the League Base Ball Season, 1886. New Yorks *vs.* Bostons. Original print by F. L. Howe, New York.

Howe was a prize-winning photographer.

275. FOOTBALL TEAMS IN ACTION: 1889

Foot-ball, Cornell *vs.* Rochester, October 19, 1889, by Seneca Roy Stoddard, Glens Falls, N. Y.

Stoddard devoted most of his career to photographing scenery, resorts, and historic sites, but occasionally ventured into other fields. Most photographs of athletic teams in this period are posed studio pictures, and this one showing action is rather unusual. LC–USZ62–11030

276. COMING INTO THE HOME STRETCH: 1887

Horse race, track and place not identified. Original print by George Barker, the noted photographer of Niagara Falls.

This is one of the photographs that won Barker a prize at an exhibition in St. Louis in 1886.

277. VANDERBILT CUP AUTO RACE: 1905

Lancia Rounding Guinea Woods Turn in Vanderbilt Cup Race, October 14, 1905. By F. Ed. Spooner, of the firm of Spooner & Wells, New York.

Spooner also distributed pictures of the overland New York to Paris auto race in 1908, sponsored by the *New York Times* and the Paris *Le*

74

FOOT-BALL GAME, CORNELL VS. ROCHESTER, 1889. (See entry 275.)

Matin. The cup race was sponsored by William K. Vanderbilt, Jr.   LC–USZ62–11031

278. THE BRIGHT FACE OF DANGER: 1890

Dixon Crossing Niagara on a 7/8 Inch Wire, by George Barker.

Barker's home was in Niagara Falls, of which he took many strikingly beautiful pictures. Dixon was a celebrated tightrope walker.

LC–USZ62–11018

279. EAST-SIDE DAREDEVIL: 1886

Steve Brodie. Original print, photographer not identified.

Brodie was a well-known stunt artist of the eighties, whose motto was that of Sam Patch— "Some things can be done as well as others." He is credited with jumping from the Brooklyn Bridge in a 140-foot plunge into the East River on July 23, 1886.

280. THE CIRCUS IS COMING TO TOWN: 1900

Ringling Parade, Columbus, Ohio. From the circus collection donated to the Library of Congress by P. M. McClintock, Franklin, Pa.

The circus was in its full glory around the turn of the century, and no parade was complete without a tootling steam calliope, like this one being played by Nellie Dunigan.   LC–USZ62–11038

281. VACATIONING IN THE ADIRONDACKS: 1889

Blue Mountain Lake House, by Seneca Roy Stoddard, Glens Falls, N. Y.

Stoddard was one of the most noted scenic photographers of the period 1870–1915, and compiled many picture albums featuring mainly the Adirondacks, Saratoga, Lake George, and Mount McGregor. This view shows a typical summer

75

hotel of the late 19th century, with big verandas and coaching parties. LC–USZ62–10933

282. VERANDA LIFE IN THE MOUNTAINS: 1889

Ralph's, Chateaugay Lake, Adirondacks, by Seneca Roy Stoddard, Glens Falls, N. Y.

The Stoddard collection contains many views of hotel interiors, children on vacation, roads in the woods, hunting, canoeing, fishing, and private summer homes—a complete survey of mountain vacationing. LC–USZ62–11011

283. ATLANTIC CITY IN THE GAY NINETIES: 1897

The Three Graces, by B. W. Kilburn, Littleton, N. H.

A posed picture, of course, showing the billowy "bathing" costume of the time for ladies. This is one of a series illustrating life at the famous resort—children, pony rides, the boardwalk, the hoky-poky ice cream man, etc.

LC–USZ62–11050

Arts and Literature

284. OLE BULL, WIZARD OF THE VIOLIN: 1810–80

From a portrait by Mathew B. Brady or one of his assistants.

From his native Norway Bull went to Germany and France to study music, and in spite of serious obstacles to his career made himself a master of astonishing skill. After a début in Paris in the presence of the great Paganini, he made triumphant tours throughout Europe and America. He married and settled in the United States, and encouraged Norwegian interest in America. LC–BH82–4867

285. REMBRANDT PEALE, PAINTER OF FAMOUS AMERICANS: 1778–1860

From a wet plate photograph by Mathew B. Brady.

After studying with his painter father, Charles Willson Peale, and with Benjamin West, he became one of America's most capable portraitists. Among his works were portraits of Thomas Jefferson, Dolley Madison, Commodore Perry, Admiral Decatur, and George Washington. Chief Justice John Marshall called the Washington portrait the most lifelike one he knew. When Mathew B. Brady took his portrait, Peale was the only living artist who had depicted Washington from life. LC–BH82–5238

286. CHESTER HARDING, SELF-TAUGHT PAINTER: 1792–1866

From a daguerreotype.

Harding was the firstborn of a remarkable group of native American painters who flourished in the nineteenth century. A Massachusetts tanner, he learned his art by himself, and painted well-known portraits of Daniel Webster and Congressman John Randolph of Roanoke. He became a favorite portraitist in London, patronized by some of the royal family.

LC–BH824–4665

287. ASHER B. DURAND, LANDSCAPE ARTIST: 1796–1886

From a daguerreotype.

Originally an engraver from New Jersey, Durand gained fame with his superb engraving of John Trumbull's painting of the signing of the Declaration of Independence. After 1835 he acquired additional note as a master painter of portraits, including those of Andrew Jackson and Henry Clay, and as a large-scale landscapist. He and Thomas Cole founded the group known as the "American Landscape School."

LC–USZ62–7648

288. WILLIAM SIDNEY MOUNT, PAINTER OF AMERICAN LIFE: 1807–68

From a portrait by Mathew B. Brady.

Mount's boyhood and youth among the country folk of Long Island inspired a lifelong interest in scenes of rural America. In his early twenties he was already famous for this type of painting, and he is now recognized as the originator of the Amer-

DIXON CROSSING THE NIAGARA GORGE ON A WIRE, 1890. *From a stereograph.* (See entry 278.)

ican school devoted to it. He is noted for depicting Negroes, and for the unaffected sense of humor that shows in his pictures. LC–BH82–4643

289. CHARLES L. ELLIOTT, POPULAR PORTRAITIST: 1812–68

From a portrait by Mathew B. Brady.

Elliott abandoned a promising career as an architectural draftsman to study painting, and for a while worked in the studio of John Trumbull. After 10 years as a wandering artist in his native upstate New York, he settled in New York City and soon was one of the most sought-after portrait painters of his time. He is said to have executed 700 likenesses, one of which was displayed at the Paris Exhibition as typically American.

LC–BH82–5207

290. FREDERICK E. CHURCH, LANDSCAPE PAINTER: 1826–1900

From an unreproduced portrait by Mathew B. Brady.

THE FASHIONABLE SHAPE, ACTRESS ANNA HELD, 1900. (See entry 306.)

Church began by depicting scenes in his native Connecticut, and became noted for his views of the Catskill Mountain region of New York, his home for many years. Later he attracted attention by large-scale canvases of scenes in South America, Greece, and the Near East. Many considered his painting of Niagara Falls the most successful one ever made.

LC–BH82–5209

291. WILLIAM CULLEN BRYANT, POET AND EDITOR: 1794–1878

From a portrait by Mathew B. Brady.

While still a youth among the Berkshire Hills of his native Massachusetts, Bryant became the first really great poet to celebrate the beauties of the American forest and field. In New York, where he lived for most of his life, he edited the *Evening Post*, set a high standard of integrity for American journalism, and cast his influence on the side of honorable politics. LC–BH834–13

292. EDGAR ALLAN POE, SPINNER OF STRANGE TALES: 1809–49

From a daguerreotype by Mathew B. Brady.

Even as a youth Poe was a controversial figure in American literary circles, well-known for the haunting music of his poems. He became one of the ablest of American editors and reviewers, and a master of the short story. In mystery tales, which he introduced to America, he reached his fullest expression of extraordinary imagination, exquisite sense of form, and acute logical and analytical power. LC–BH834–34

293. WASHINGTON IRVING, GRACEFUL STYLIST: 1783–1859

From a daguerreotype by Mathew B. Brady, made in the 1850's.

Throughout a long life devoted to literature and diplomacy, Irving never lost the light, gentle touch first displayed in humorous newspaper sketches and in his *Knickerbocker's History of New York*. Other literary triumphs were his biographies of Columbus and of Washington, and his narrative of Captain Bonneville's western explorations. To most people he will always be the mellow and charming author of *The Sketch Book*, and

the gracious host of "Sunnyside," his Hudson River home, a mecca for authors.

LC–BH824–4900

294. NATHANIEL HAWTHORNE, ROMANCER LIGHT AND SOMBRE: 1804–64

From a daguerreotype by Mathew B. Brady.

The novelist of antique New England and popular writer of tales for children is shown in his middle years, when he was writing *The Scarlet Letter* and *The House of the Seven Gables*.

LC–BH8277–518

295. WILLIAM H. PRESCOTT, CHRONICLER OF SPANISH CONQUERORS: 1796–1859

From an original daguerreotype by Mathew B. Brady.

In spite of the crippling handicap of poor vision, Massachusetts-born Prescott became the first internationally famous American historian. The brilliant reception of his *History of the Reign of Ferdinand and Isabella* in 1837 introduced the triumphs of his lucid and entertaining stories of the Spanish conquests in Mexico and Peru. He achieved rare success in blending exhaustive research and literary artistry. LC–BH824–5152

296. GEORGE BANCROFT, HISTORIAN OF DEMOCRATIC AMERICA: 1800–91

From a portrait by Mathew B. Brady.

In the galaxy of Massachusetts authors Bancroft holds a brilliant place as a linguist, philosopher and historian, known to the chief scholars of Europe. He is still respected by countrymen who read his popular and panoramic history of the United States, published between 1834 and 1874 in 10 volumes. He served as Minister to Great Britain and to Prussia, and as Secretary of the Navy he planned and established the Naval Academy at Annapolis. LC–BH82–5157

297. HORACE GREELEY, DEAN OF JOURNALISTS: 1811–72

From an original wet plate by Mathew B. Brady or one of his assistants.

The New Hampshire country boy, who learned

journalism in the hard school of New York, made his New York *Tribune* a model newspaper, a national institution, an oracle of opinion. People laughed at his eccentricities of dress and thought, but respected his courage and high ideals, and his defense of free inquiry and humane causes. The fiasco of his candidacy for President in 1872 has not obscured his work for national unity and good journalism. LC–BH82–23

298. HORACE GREELEY AS A YOUNG MAN

From a daguerreotype made some time in the 1840's. LC–USZ62–8776

299. JAMES GORDON BENNETT, INNOVATOR IN JOURNALISM: 1795–1872

From a daguerreotype by Mathew B. Brady.

As a youth Bennett came from Scotland to America, and he worked his way up from proofreading to be a Washington correspondent, winning fame for his reports of proceedings in Congress. As owner and editor Bennett made his New York *Herald* the most valuable newspaper property in the Nation. He introduced articles on the money market, distribution by carriers, and interviews with celebrities, and was the first to use the telegraph for news dispatches.

LC–BH8277–545

The Theater

300. EDWIN FORREST, MELODRAMATIC ACTOR: 1806–72

From a portrait by Mathew B. Brady.

At 14 Forrest made his first stage appearance in his native Philadelphia, and 6 years later his playing of Othello was a hit in New York. Later he repeated his success in London, and became a friend of the renowned actors Kemble and Macready. Wealth enabled him to retire in middle life, but he returned to the New York stage to star in *Hamlet*. He was most noted for his roles of Macbeth, King Lear, and Othello.

LC–BH8277–519

301. CHARLOTTE CUSHMAN (1816–76) AS MEG MERRILIES

From a portrait by Mathew B. Brady or one of his assistants.

The great Boston actress first appeared on the stage in 1834, and next year starred as Lady Macbeth. She became celebrated as Meg Merrilies and for her playing of Shakespearean roles, especially Lady Macbeth, Rosalind, and Romeo, and was in great demand as a dramatic reader. In 1844 she played with the English actor Macready on a long tour of the United States. The poet William Cullen Bryant in 1874 publicly presented her with a laurel wreath in token of the Nation's respect. LC–BH82–5353

302. CLARA L. KELLOGG, POPULAR CONCERT SINGER: 1842–1916

From a portrait by Mathew B. Brady or an assistant.

From South Carolina Miss Kellogg went for her musical education to New York, and there first appeared on the opera stage in 1861, at the old Academy of Music. Her repertoire finally included 45 operas, and in the 1870's she established an English and an Italian opera company. She was one of America's best-known and most admired concert singers, and in retirement wrote her popular *Memoirs of an American Prima Donna* (1913). LC–BH82–4694

303. ADELINA PATTI, OPERA STAR: 1843–1919

From a portrait by Mathew B. Brady.

Born in Spain of Italian parents, Adelina Patti was educated and trained in New York, and at the age of 7 was well-known as a concert singer. Her début was followed by many brilliant years, especially in Italian opera, in London, Paris, and Madrid, due not only to her pure voice but also to her personal charm. At the age of 60 she still thrilled audiences on a long American concert tour. LC–BH8277–628

304. FAMOUS DANCERS OF LONG AGO

Laura Le Claire and Lottie Forbes posed for this portrait by Mathew B. Brady or one of his assistants. LC–BH82–4669

305. ONE OF HARRY KELLAR'S PUZZLERS: 1889

"Astarte." A New Aerial Illusion Exhibited by Kellar; from Negative by Flash-Light. By Rothengatter & Dillon, Philadelphia.

An early example of flashlight technique—was the lady suspended or not? LC–USZ62–10930

306. THE FASHIONABLE SHAPE: 1900

Actress Anna Held, by Aime Dupont, Fifth Avenue, New York.

She was a kind of symbol of the true gaiety of the Gay Nineties. LC–USZ62–11046

307. MAXINE, THE MAGNIFICENT: 1890's

Maxine Elliott, by the Byron Studio, New York, a pioneer in photography of the theater.

Miss Elliott came from Maine, studied for the stage with the celebrated Dion Boucicault, and became a foremost actress while in Augustin Daly's company. Famous in both England and America and noted for her beauty, she played with the leading stage personalities of her time, and in 1908 built her own theater in New York. LC–USZ62–10924

308. GREAT LADY OF THE THEATER: ca. 1900

Ethel Barrymore, by the Byron Studio, New York.

Her father Maurice was an actor, as were her two brothers, John and Lionel. By 1900 she was a star of the New York stage, under the auspices of Charles Frohman. A star she remained for two generations, in a wide variety of roles on the stage, and finally as an astounding success in motion pictures. LC–USZ62–10923

309. MRS. MINNIE MADDERN FISKE AS "TESS": 1897

Scene from Thomas Hardy's "Tess of the D'Urbervilles," by the Byron Studio, New York.

The adopted name of Marie Augusta Davey came from her first stage part, at the age of three, as "Little Minnie Maddern," and that name remained on the billboards and in the lights until she died in 1932. She starred with the greatest actors and actresses of her time, and had a distinguished career as a director, and as an encourager of young playwrights.

LC–USZ62–11039

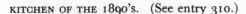

KITCHEN OF THE 1890's. (See entry 310.)

THE HOME CIRCLE, 1889. *From a stereograph.* (See entry 312.)

Home and Children

310. KITCHEN OF THE NINETIES

By C. H. Currier.
From the collection of Ernst Halberstadt, Boston.

In the period 1890–1900 Currier was employed to take "record" photographs of homes, offices,

work, and amusements in or near Boston, presenting a picture of life in the Gay Nineties. Note the old-fashioned gas and coal stoves, and the pies and bread on the table.   LC–USZ62–11016

311. SATURDAY NIGHT

From a stereograph by George Barker.

A boy is shown being scrubbed. Although they seem very naive today, such posed and sentimental views were very popular before 1900 and along with scenery were the stock-in-trade of the huge stereograph business.   LC–USZ62–11005

312. THE HOME CIRCLE, 1889

By B. W. Kilburn, Littleton, N. H.
A group of mothers and children.
LC–USZ62–11009

313. DOMESTIC DENTISTRY, 1897

By B. W. Kilburn, Littleton, N. H.
A boy having a tooth pulled by his mother.
LC–USZ62–11054

314. SCHOOL ATHLETICS IN WASHINGTON: *ca.* 1899

Western High School Girls Playing Basketball, by Frances Benjamin Johnston.
Miss Johnston, one of the eminent American "documentary" photographers, made an extensive series of photographs of all phases of activity in the Washington public schools. These she exhibited at the Third International Congress of Photography, Paris, 1900, at which she was the only woman delegate.   LC–USZ62–4543

Life and Sentiment

315. A NEARLY FORGOTTEN OCCUPATION

Cutting Ice, by C. H. Currier. From the collection of Ernst Halberstadt, Boston.
Before the days of the Frigidaire men waited for a long "cold snap" to cut pond ice into blocks for storage in huge wooden icehouses.
LC–USZ62–10922

316. AN ALMOST FORGOTTEN SPORT: 1890's

Curling on the Pond, near Boston, by C. H. Currier. From the collection of Ernst Halberstadt, Boston.
This is one of a series of "record" photographs

of home life, work, and amusements in and around Boston—a picture of life in the Nineties.
LC–USZ62–10920

317. A TYPICAL "SENTIMENTAL"

The Haunted Lane, by L. M. Melander & Bro.
A bit of trick photography is used to depict a ghost. This is one of a large collection of stereographs made in the period 1876–89 by this firm, which specialized in such work.
LC–USZ62–11053

318. THE MARTIAL SPIRIT OF '98

"My Country Calls, and I Must Go." From a stereograph by B. W. Kilburn.
Nearly every commercial photographer of this period turned out large quantities of "sentimentals" for an apparently greedy market. They were somewhat mawkish, and sometimes mildly naughty. Today they constitute a valuable record of American life and humor 60 years ago.
LC–USZ62–11006

A Group of Studies: 1887-1901

A GROUP OF "STUDIES": 1887–1901

Posed "studies" were enormously popular in the period 1880–1900, and were framed to hang in innumerable homes in place of more expensive paintings. The succeeding eight examples illustrate the variety of subjects treated in this branch of photographic art.

319. MAN, KNOW THY DESTINY

Original print by Landy of Cincinnati, Ohio, 1887.
This was one of the Blair Prize Cup pictures at the Photographers' Association of America, Chicago, August 12, 1887.

320. TWELFTH NIGHT, 1889

The carouse in the kitchen. Original print by an unidentified photographer.

THE HAUNTED LANE. *From a "sentimental" stereograph.* (See entry 317.)

321. ENOCH ARDEN, 1890

Original print by an unidentified photographer. A scene from the famous poem (the subject of a popular play) by Alfred Lord Tennyson.

322. WHO'S SKEERED

Original print by T. E. Dillon, Scranton, Pa., 1897.

323. A PRESENT FOR GRANDPA

Original print, "composition picture," by E. Donald Roberts, Detroit, Mich., 1898.

324. PALOMA SCHRAMM & TEACHER

(Music lesson.) Original print by F. M. Stiffler, 1898.

325. COMFORT

Original print by unidentified photographer, 1899.

326. THE TRAVELING COBBLER

Original print by E. Willard Spurr, Decorah, Iowa, 1901.

Some Later Cameras:
1871-1900

327. CAMERA, AMERICAN, FOR 4 x 5 GLASS PLATES: 1871

Patented in October 1871. Lent by the George Eastman House.

The cover of the box folds back on hinges, revealing a bellows-view camera. There are sliding circular doors, and a mirror at the front and back for ground-glass viewing, as well as two optical view-finders for vertical or horizontal pictures.

328. "DETECTIVE CAMERA": 1883

An American model for 4x5 glass plates, invented in 1883. Lent by the George Eastman House.

This wooden camera with brass fittings has removable ground glass and plateholder concealed by a door in the back, and a spring-driven rotary shutter concealed by a sliding door on the front board. It was focused by telescoping the back box, containing the plateholder, into the front box containing the lens and shutter. This was one of the first cameras completely adapted for hand-held exposures, and for this reason was called a "detective camera."

329. CONCEALED VEST CAMERA: AMERICAN: 1886

Patented by R. D. Gray, New York, and distributed by Anthony & Scovil Co. Lent by the George Eastman House.

This camera was intended to be suspended from the neck of the operator and worn under both coat and vest, with the lens protruding through the buttonhole of the vest. It is made of nickel-plated metal and has a circular plate for six exposures. The shutter is a spring-driven rotary type, wound as the plate is rotated, and is released by a string coming through the bottom of the camera and concealed in the pocket.

330. FIRST MODEL OF THE KODAK: 1888

Made and marketed by George Eastman expressly for roll film. Lent by the George Eastman House.

This camera, with its name coined by Eastman, was the product of much patient experimentation. It was marketed in July 1888 and patented on September 4. It weighs only 22 ounces, cost $25, and made a picture 2½ inches in diameter. The roll-holder is an integral part, and the film made 100 exposures. The exposed roll was sent to Rochester to be processed. This camera created a new class of patrons and eventually started a new business, that of the photofinisher. The first Kodak designed for dealer-processing was the pocket Kodak of 1895.

331. CENTURY FOLDING HAND CAMERA: *ca.* 1900

Distributed by the Century Camera Co., and intended for 6½ x 8½ plates. Lent by the George Eastman House.

This was manufactured by the Eastman Kodak Co., which supplied a roll-holder at the factory for making 50 pictures. It is fitted with a 6½ x 8½ Bausch & Lomb Plastigmat lens (marked U. S. 3) and a pneumatic shutter, with speeds of 3 seconds and 1/100 second, and a lever to change to time exposures.

332. CAMERA FOR 4 x 5 GLASS PLATES, AMERICAN: 1900

Made by the American Camera Co., Rochester, N. Y. Lent by the George Eastman House.

This press-type folding hand camera has a Rauber & Wollensak shutter with an 8″ rapid rectilinear lens-stop U. S. 8, shutter speeds 1 second to 1/100 second, bulb and time.

AERIAL VIEW OF BOSTON, 1860. *From a wet plate.* (See entry 334a.)

86

Interesting Uses

333. EARLY USE IN ASTRONOMY: 1853

Photograph of the moon, frontispiece to *The Photographic Art Journal*, vol. 6, 1853.

This probably is one of the first photographs of the moon taken from the United States. This copy is a "crystalotype" of a daguerreotype taken by John A. Whipple in March 1851. (*See* vol. 6, 1853, p. 66.)

334. FIRST SUCCESSFUL AMERICAN AERIAL PHOTOGRAPH: 1860

"Boston As the Eagle and the Wild Goose See It" (Oliver Wendell Holmes). By Samuel A. King and James Wallace Black, frontispiece to *The Photo-Miniature*, July 1903.

The view was taken from Prof. Samuel Archer King's balloon on October 13, 1860, by James Wallace Black, Boston Photographer of the firm of Black & Batchelder. King was a well-known aeronaut, active until his death in 1914. The picture was exhibited for a week in Boston, and caused intense excitement.

334a. MODERN PRINT OF THE "BALLOON VIEW" OF BOSTON: 1908

"Boston, Mass. Balloon View in 1861." Copy print, sepia tone.

This print of the famous King and Black view, taken from a captive balloon, was deposited in the Library of Congress for copyright on March 2, 1908. Although the date when the picture was taken is stated (on the back) to have been in 1861, it really was in October 1860. (See entries 334, 335.)　　　　　　　　LC–USZ62–10911

335. CONTEMPORARY ACCOUNTS OF THE BALLOON PHOTOGRAPH: 1860

"Aerostation," scrapbook of James Allen, volume I, 1857–92. Opened to newspaper articles on the balloon photography of James Wallace Black and Samuel A. King over Boston.

"The Late Balloon Photographing Experiment" was written by King of the well-known firm of King & Allen, aeronauts. Many accounts appeared in contemporary magazines and newspapers, and the photograph was reproduced in an article in *Life*, June 5, 1939.

336. STEREOGRAPHIC PROOFS BY THE LANGENHEIM BROTHERS: 1856

Four sheets, with 24 mounted salted-paper proofs, from an album of views taken by Frederick and William Langenheim of Philadelphia.

The Langenheim brothers are believed to have been the first American photographers to produce stereographs commercially. The album originally contained 483 views.

337. AN EARLY SCENIC SERIES: 1859

Photographic Scrap Book, by Franklin White, Lancaster, N. H.

This volume was deposited, to copyright the photographs, in the clerk's office of the United States District Court for New Hampshire. It consists of 11 pages of small prints, mostly oval, of scenes in the White Mountains and in and around Quebec, and is said to be one of the earliest series of its kind made in America. In the 1850's photographers began to realize the great market for scenic albums.

COPYRIGHTING OF PHOTOGRAPHS

By an act of Congress passed in 1870 the Library of Congress received many volumes of old copyright records which had been kept in the offices of the clerks of the United States district courts. These records contain a considerable number of photographs deposited for copyright, including some of special interest.

338. COLORADO TERRITORY: 1864–70

Opened to George D. Wakely's striking photographs of towns and scenery.

339. CALIFORNIA: 1867–79

Photographic portraits of Carl Schurz, by Bayley & Winters, September 3, 1869.

These were made for a series of cards, probably to enhance the political prestige of the brilliant German-American editor, author, and Republican leader. At the time, Schurz was United States Senator from Missouri; later he became Secretary of the Interior under President Hayes.

340. GEORGIA, SOUTHERN DISTRICT: 1866–70

Photographic portraits of Generals Robert E. Lee and J. E. Johnston, by D. J. Ryan, Savannah, made by special permission for the Ladies' Memorial Association.

341. RHODE ISLAND: 1857–70

Photographs of Ida Lewis and her home, 1869, by Manchester Bros., probably made for George Douglas Brewerton's book, *Ida Lewis, the Heroine of Lime Rock* (Newport, 1869).

Miss Lewis, the daughter of the lighthouse keeper at the rock, became famous for her rescues of people from the perils of the sea, and received honors, letters, and gifts from all over the world.

342. NEW JERSEY: 1846–69

The entries for March 1 and 2, 1869, illustrate rather unusual cases of copyrighting photographs. One is for a freakish "Steam Wagon" contraption manufactured by Winans, Eno & Co.; the other shows molded plaster ornaments for ceiling center-pieces, by William H. Riker.

Albums

343. FAMILY ALBUM, *ca.* 1860–1900

Presented to the Library of Congress by the estate of Victor S. Clark, noted economist, authority on labor and immigration, editor of *The Living Age*, and author of *History of Manufactures in the United States*. The volume is full of unidentified carte-de-visite portraits, probably of members of Clark's family. Opened to portraits of Abraham Lincoln and a Civil War general.

344. PARLOR ALBUM, *ca.* 1870–80

Given to the Library of Congress by Roy E. Stryker, a noted photographer.

Displayed to show the tooled-leather cover, gold lettering and clasp typical of the albums of

that period. It contains many portrait photographs, some of them autographed.

345. AN ALBUM ON LUMBERING: 1892

Cummer Lumber Company Collection. Photographs of lumbering operations by William Worrall Harmer of Cadillac, Mich. Copyright deposit, 1892.

A typical use of photography for commercial purposes, intended to illustrate all phases of the industry.

346. A COLLECTOR'S ALBUM ON RAILROADS: 1890–1910

Collector's Record Photographs of American Locomotives, etc.

This is one of two albums containing over 300 photographs of railroad equipment on the Boston & Albany, New York, New Haven & Hartford, Erie, and Central Railroad of New Jersey. There are also pictures of streetcars, stagecoaches, and railroad covered bridges.

347. ALBUM OF THE SAN FRANCISCO EARTHQUAKE: 1906

Arnold Genthe's original album of contact print proofs of small photographs of the earthquake and fire.

The collection of original negatives is in the San Francisco Palace of the Legion of Honor. Genthe, of German birth, came to America in 1895 as a classical scholar, and became a celebrated artistic photographer, a compiler of picture books, and one of the first American photographers to use natural-color plates.

348. A TYPICAL COLLEGE CLASS ALBUM: 1868

Yale University, Class of 1868.

This is one of two albums, containing portraits of members of the class and of the faculty, class groups and clubs, pictures of the campus and its buildings, and portraits of local "characters." It was presented to the Library of Congress in 1924 by Prof. Richard A. Rice, former Chief of the Prints Division.

88